9789030653394

D1775948

COUNTRY DIARY

COUNTRY DIARY

MATT MUNDELL

GORDON WRIGHT PUBLISHING
55 MARCHMONT ROAD, EDINBURGH, EH9 1HT
SCOTLAND

© Matt Mundell 1981

No part of this publication may be reproduced, stored in a retrieval system, or transmitted, in any form or by any means electronic, mechanical, photocopying, recording or otherwise, without prior permission of the publisher.

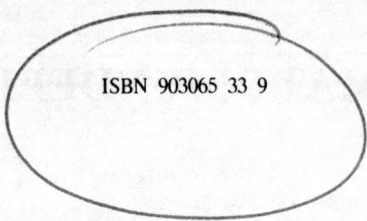

ISBN 903065 33 9

Typeset by Image Services (Edinburgh) Limited

PREFACE

Stravaiging homewards many a night through hill glens in the winter of 1965-66 after I had rejoined *The Scottish Farmer*, the winking lights in upland farm and cottage windows worried me. They meant, almost certainly, that families were seated round the television.

At these same firesides many years before, there were cheerier times, as in the glow from the hearth, the tales and legends of the glens, their people and their stock were handed down through the generations.

I determined then, that each winter I would rake the sheep country and seek out the worthies and retell their yarns—true, on the verge of truth or even otherwise—and pass on to others an account of their thoughts, their deeds, their work, their sorrows and their successes. Little did I realise how much I would personally become involved.

For fourteen happy years I badgered, confused, quizzed, held back and probably inconvenienced many of the country's hill people while gathering material. I spent hundreds of cheery nights at distant firesides in the kindly valleys of Wales, the northern English dales and throughout Scotland from the Cheviots to the Pentland Firth. It is unfortunate that in these pages I can only present a selection of the stories and a few of the people I sojourned with. My sincere thanks to everyone for their co-operation and companionship.

William Laidlaw snr., that worthy editor of the *Annandale Observer*, first set me on a variety of journalistic assignments during my cub reporting days, and my ex-editors George Millar and Angus MacDonald of *The Scottish Farmer* gave me the chance to travel to the land's furthermost points to meet and write of characters whose wisdom and ways are vanishing.

The whole aspect of meeting in with the hill folk has been even better than working!

To all these people this book is ungrudgingly dedicated.

Matt Mundell.

ACKNOWLEDGEMENTS

The author, it seems, is not the only one involved in the compilation of a book.

I am very grateful to my former photographic colleagues on *The Scottish Farmer,* especially David Todd, John Fraser and Niall Robertson who took most of the photographs which appear in this book.

Thanks are also due to Mrs. J. Troughton, Loftus Brown, Tom Phin, J. Glenn Crawford, Hugh Thompson, Jack Fraser, the B.B.C., *The Farmer's Weekly,* Marc Henrie, the National Museum of Antiquities of Scotland, Country Life Section and the Ewart Library Dumfries, who kindly gave permission to reproduce photographs.

Thanks also to Joe Johnstone and Tony Iley and the families of the late John Dickson and Tom Murray for permission to reproduce selections from their poetry.

Acknowledgement is also due to *The Scotsman* who nowadays publish my regular ramblings, some of which are reproduced here.

Above all, my warmest thanks go to my wife Anne and my daughters Margot and Kathleen for their tolerance and understanding over the years during lengthy periods of absence, either away from home or out-of-bounds, day and night, at the typewriter.

There's a good time coming.

M. M.

CONTENTS

A PERTHSHIRE LAMBING

If things are going well, all countryside jobs for the shepherd and the farmer are satisfying. When things start to go wrong it can be a different picture. Of all the duties carried out by hill shepherds, the most critical and arduous is the lambing which can bring success, disappointment or disaster.

"Any volunteers," the flockmaster shouted in the byre doorway at an hour somewhere mid-way between midnight and the city dweller's stirring time.

Without need to repeat his plea, two came forward. Workers who did not need to be told what they had volunteered for — a fifteen-hour stint on the 1,000 ft line over the heather, peat moss, lazy-beds, corries, waterfalls, dykes and fences.

On the long rib of ground lounging three and a half miles back over Callander in Perthshire, the black and white alert listener Cap and the black, jag-eared Glen — so keen always to get to a brae-top to see what lay beyond — took naturally to Robin Wood's heel and to the sheep pad running aloft behind the steading.

Headed upwards and across to study every hollow, bog, knowe and hill face. To see if the 'Minister' was settled; to check the progress of 'Easter Monday,' to smile (and working collies can smile) like their master at the antics of the loping 'Roadrunner'; to see if McTurk or the Dollarman and others of their ilk had fathered a prospective money-making tup lamb with the glint of eye, horn and wool that only a true sheepman knows.

Just another day in the hill lambing for Cap and Glen. And like every other day in the upland flockmaster and shepherds' busiest time, about to unveil its surprises, successes and sorrows.

Poets have written much of the lambing season but mostly about the sight and gambols of the white youngsters. (Many shepherds with far more rhyme and wise philosophy to their ways could do it much better). Few have caught the unknownness that lies ahead each morning as the shepherd's crop grows among the rushes, by dykebacks and burnsides as April leans forward into May in either its summer rig-out or winter plaid of sleet and swirling east-winders.

And they have possibly not seen nature's kindness and cruelty, blessings and rebuffs as have the likes of Robin Wood and Duncan McLaren whose 536 Blackface ewes rake the rim of West Perthshire heights and hopefully

9

—that time I spent some days at the lambing—would rear in the region of 700 lambs.

The couthy old black-collared ewe, the 'Minister' had already done her stuff. The 'Roadrunner' with the gait of an ostrich, was rearing a single lamb. His young life was frustrating—a quick suck of nourishment, and then his mobile milk bar took off, for 'Roadrunner' black of face and with a stride like Stephenson's Rocket deemed it necessary to bolt always to the farthest corner from human presence. Robin's wife, Helena, at the lambings herself drawing in the twin lambs to lower pasture, named the ewe, when trying once to walk it home. At least, that was one of the names.

No sheep on 1,800-acre West Bracklinn covered more ground at such speed for so many hours of the day. Certainly not little 'Easter Monday' who was bulking up. But this was perhaps more because of human kindness, for his mother, who dropped him on holiday week-end, was not too maternally inclined, and he knew the sight of a human meant the lambing bag and a milk bottle.

That bag, though simple, is like dog and stick—a sheepman's necessity. With Balsam oil to help ease difficult lambings, antibiotics for any ewes which had to be handled, calcium which, far out on the hill, can save many a beast, and an old metal lambing aid, rarely needed, but on hand should there be a particularly bad case of a ewe being unable to lamb herself.

So much can happen on a day's round in the peak of hill lambing. Life and death, hope and despair. "I used to be up and down with it. If there were two or three dead lambs I would be depressed but would be happy enough with a fair crop that day." said Robin, a town boy—his father Jack was once a fish and chip shop owner—who got off primary school to help at lambings. With self-education and advice from many others, linked to hard experience, he had built his life.

He partnered Duncan McLaren, who, when I visited in 1976, had seen seventy-one lambings 'man and boy' on the West Bracklinn ground where the hill is split into three blocks and four hill parks as well as seventy acres of better inbye ground to carry the stock of ewes, hoggs and a small suckler cow herd.

The days of the ups and downs are past now for Robin. He takes everything in his stride. But the mystery faculty which thirls a man to sheep, dogs and hills, grows stronger every year as each ewe and her parentage, her behaviour, her habits and her potential become memorised. The hill men call it 'kenning.' A 'guid kenner' knows each animal, the ground she covers, her daughters and sons. Whether they lamb easily or have problems. Whether or not they have much milk to feed their lambs.

Lambing time for Robin meant a 5.30 a.m. start, returning off the hill five hours and many miles later for a welcome breakfast. Back into the inbye fields to sort out and move twins to lower paddocks or make sure

10

mothered-on lambs were taking to their new charges, and then home again for a snack. Then back to the lengthy hill round from 2 p.m. to darkness.

"I wouldn't do these kind of hours for anything else but sheep," said Robin, who added that what kept him going is the "dour determination to get good lambs and good stock." Some flockmasters have said it takes three generations of sheep—fifteen years—to do so, but Robin feels this is an under-estimation. Priority is sound stock that will breed regularly and maybe later he can refine their looks to his liking.

Biggest lambing time problem—"getting up in the morning," quipped Helena—is the weather. Duncan McLaren could easily recall 1947, a year every hill man talks about in a depressed voice. But 1948 was a good year. There have been several severe ones since, especially in the late 1970's.

"I live all the year round for the lambing coming around," said Robin, who annually at the big Blackface ram sales is looking for prospective sires which will bring the farming partners at West Bracklinn a more uniform ewe stock. Maybe too some day a good tup lamb to sell themselves, as well as the bread and butter store lambs. Each lamb then, is studied as soon as he comes upon it to see its potential. "It is the unknown, the expectation, that is the thing," said Robin.

Each morning the hill man's domain of hefts, hirsels, stells, buchts, lunkies and parricks (small paddocks) starts around daylight to unveil its varied chapters. A cuckoo had a half-hearted hiccup up by scenic Bracklinn Falls when we set off—she chorussed like a long-player the next morning—and this is a good omen. The old worthies say things go better after the cuckoo has called. But any sheep which is lean before then does not have a great future.

The sun hit the south-lying face about 6 a.m. Three roe deer flashed tail-stubs as they leapt over a fence into the trees. A solitary ewe which had watched our progress with Cap and Glen settled down duly to produce her offspring in quiet privacy once we had gone past. Several times ewes gave birth to their lambs only minutes after we had passed.

The old girl who had watched us was of Newton Stewart blood. Breeders have their own preferences—Lanark, Stirling, Perth or Newton Stewart depending on the type of wool required or the strains' various attributes which are argued about at any sheep sale, sheepdog trial, or mart public house. Newton blood now dominates West Bracklinn stock. Very successfully too.

So every lamb was studied to see what stamp his or her sire had left. Particular attention was paid to progeny of Robin's dearer rams, Dollarman and McTurk. Helena always asked about them when Robin got home. The search—though the farm was run on purely commercial stock lines—was for a tup lamb either off these two sires or others with alert ears, bonny colours and the magical glint. If not, then sizey ewe lambs which would do for better replacement stock, another step in improvement.

11

Ewes parentage was described. They could be off a sire from the Gass flock; by rams bought from Larg of Creetown, or Allanfaulds or elsewhere. Not only that, their grandfathers and grand-dams were known. Even at birth the texture, shape, size and marking of the lamb could determine whether it's sire would be retained for use another year.

"There's another pair of old Newton Stewarts over there," said Robin. "They will be lambing today." A fox barked out away near a far plantation. A bleating ewe standing by a hill drain was approached. "She is being answered so the lamb must be alright," said Robin, and sure enough when we got there the lamb was healthy but unable to get a foothold to climb out of the deep drain. Every piece of ground was walked and studied and for good reason.

By the side of another burn a lamb remained still, her dam cropping a few yards away. A tragedy? No, "Up ye get, y're jeest too fu' and lazy," said Robin dispatching the surprised lamb to her mother.

More twins born overnight were studied for their future potential and for memory. For the hill man as well as knowing each ewe, must know which lambs are off each matron. A gimmer (a female having her first lamb) had a biggish lamb and a small dead one. There had been a lot of small twin lambs off gimmers that year and ideally on hill ground they would have been better and more economic with a strong single lamb.

By a deep corrie, a hoodie sat silently on a brow. On sentry duty for his mate on a nearby nest. In the afternoon when we went past again another bleating ewe drew Robin back to the gorge. At the bottom in the burn her lamb lay dead. The lamb's tongue had been nicked out by the hoodies.

Some ewes near to lambing steal a lamb from another ewe. One had done this the previous night before dropping twins herself beside a fence. She had then taken a dislike to her adopted lamb and knocked him through a fence—and down a fifty-foot drop to the same rocky burn. A fine bit of mountaineering by Robin retrieved the lamb which had miraculously halted without injury only inches from the fast-flowing water.

Ewes with dead lambs were 'twinned-on.' A lamb was taken from a gimmer with twins and the skin of the dead lamb tied over it, so that the mother scented her own offspring. Glen and Cap had a premier role in helping Robin catch either lambs or ewes—and also in steering ewes with twin lambs down off the hill into the grassier paddocks.

This was usually the afternoon chore and with maybe near 200 sets of twins it was time-consuming. Canniness is the big thing when walking the lambs. And any ewes with single lambs were turned away back to higher ground.

There are other things to see and of which to talk. West Bracklinn has a big acreage covered in lazy-beds, the cultivation method of the days when glens like this were heavily populated. Robin sometimes wishes the clock could be turned back to see folk at their tasks on these acreages.

Blackcocks in a mating dance: gangs of hares gambolling on frost-covered grass. At one point far out on the hill a ewe stood by her still-born lamb. Its tail had been nipped off. Next morning in the same area sheep were very unsettled and sticking to their ground. It was perhaps a fox to blame for both occurrences.

Marks on a sandy knowe showed one ewe had difficulty in the night giving birth and there was one ewe with a 'keb'—a dead lamb. She was taken back to the shed and marked so that she would not be retained for more breeding. Next day we found her sitting on the spot where she had given birth.

We discovered a dead ewe. Possibly through milk fever thought Robin, after studying her position and features. Her lamb was caught and put into the lambing bag and later put in beside a ewe which had lost her lamb.

One day—and a brilliantly sunny one from around 6 a.m. to 8.30 p.m. yielded thirteen sets of twins and ten singles, with two or three dead. About forty in all.

There would be better days and happier days and there would be more worrying ones, particularly if the whirls of bitterly cold east winds became stronger the following day. Possibly nature would yet take its toll of many of the lambs which were then gambolling on the quiet hill.

SILENT TRACKS

Mighty droves of cattle, sometimes stretching for miles, helped determine the routes for Scotland's glen roads. The drover had a much respected role in the country's livestock industry and general well-being. In the profession there were saints and sinners, all worthies. Only the very old— and very few at that—can recall the legendary travelling stocksmen.

If you listen carefully in the skin-tight mist shrouds there is still an echo of the hooves. Faint, sad and no more than a hushed whisper. And of a mighty drove at that.

But if you are alone and endowed with imagination, the natural bounds of hill, scree and moor, nurture the clamour of a day that is far gone on some of our land's innermost hills.

The canny drovers trudged here with plaid and porridge, kitchen reared dogs and blackthorn sticks. I have myself taken the drove tracks of our southern uplands, skirting past the bogs where they steered beasts not long off the Portpatrick boats, through the nicks of the hills. Talkative hills, for today they retell clearly the story of a wonderful past with their clearly defined green runs pinpointing the old drove roads.

Legend speaks of some 18,000 cattle a year coming off the Portpatrick boats from Ireland in the 1780's and of the glorious sight of as many as seventy-five score of Galloway cattle being seen in one drove passing through Carlisle for Norfolk. One droving record speaks of a south-bound drove five or six miles in length between Moniaive and Dunscore in Dumfriesshire.

Others have memories of the classic routes of the north. And of the men who took the stock to the famed trysts and markets. In his eighty-second year, sprightly old Alex MacDougall told me some of the tales handed down to him by his father Dugald, last of the true and renowned drovers, a white-bearded worthy whose forebears were also drovers with much of their work taking them to the Falkirk Tryst.

Black Highland cattle costing probably around £8.10s. when Gaelic-speaking Dugald and his uncles made their bargains on the isles, they came over the old walks from Mid-Argyll in drives of fifty to sixty. They had summered at upland Barmolloch at the end of Ederlin's Glen with maybe two men and two dogs doing the steerage down the stock pads used for decades by the worthy profession.

"I have heard father say that on the first two or three days you did not force your cattle. You let them walk away at their leisure. If you

14

forced them too much the first couple of days, they would never look the same," Alex MacDougall told me at his home in Clachan near Tarbert.

Dugald himself—he died in his ninety-first year in 1956—has fortunately put on record his own advice on how a good drover should be careful not to press his cattle too hard at the start of one of the long stravaigs from the Argyll hinterland. For there were good rewards from the English dealers at the Falkirk Tryst for quality, and Barmolloch's beasts had that if not pushed too hard.

"They were in full bloom, and full of flesh and hair," the late Dugald MacDougall has recorded. "If you sweated them, the hair drooped and never got up again into the same condition. The great secret was to take them there as good looking as they were when they left home.

"One would think there was nothing but drive, and force them on with a stick, but that wasn't allowed at all. They'd go quite nicely when they were left alone. There was an art in doing it right, properly; even suppose one would think it was a simple thing, there was an art in doing it properly too, to give man and beast a chance, yes."

Alex MacDougall, a sheepman all his life and with droving experience himself of moving wintered hoggs (the previous Spring's lambs) from Dalmally station the thirty-odd miles down the water line of Loch Awe past Portsonachan to Ford, had many a time heard his father tell of the drover's ways.

"He used to enjoy talking about them once he gave up that life and was farming. When they had fifty-sixty beasts in a drove he said, one man went ahead perhaps with ten or twelve cattle to lead them. If these ten or twelve went into a gap or through an open gate it meant they only had to get ten or twelve out instead of sixty."

In his own hogg drives near the south end of Loch Awe, Alex would probably be re-crossing tracks taken by his famed father heading from Barmolloch to the Falkirk Tryst, the gathering place for the main trade in the late 1800's.

Dugald's route to the Tryst had taken him over the rib of hill from Loch Awe to come out somewhere around the present Auchindrain Crofting Museum on the side of Loch Fyne. Dugald shared work with four uncles, the MacLellands who were farmers and dealers in Kilmichael Glassary parish, an airt where there used to be a Tryst.

The drover would go with his uncles to the isles in summer and spring to buy cattle and these, said Alex, were shipped on the shortest link from Jura to the Point of Knap in Knapdale. "These beasts would be there at more or less three years old. They were not very big cattle and mostly black Highland. The boats used were usually small and they used to fill the bottoms with birch branches to keep the cattles' feet from going through".

Alex's father has left for posterity some of his views on the type of cattle which made the best prices at Falkirk and so determined their attitude when bargaining on Islay. Dugald's experiences were recorded and reprinted in *Scottish Studies* in 1959 and a copy of the recording and a transcription were deposited at the School of Scottish Studies. It is a great pity many more like him departed without their tales being recorded.

Dugald has said the black cattle of the West Highlands could fetch the highest prices at Falkirk. "There was more black ones in these days. But when they got like everything else, into fancy things, they did away with the black ones. There's hardly any of the black cattle left. They wouldn't go in for crosses, not by any means. One of the uncles especially had a great horror o' crosses. Nothing but the pure Highland native cattle you know, bullocks and heifers."

On arrival at Knap, the cattle would be walked by Tayvallich, Bellanoch and Kilmichael for summering at Barmolloch. Once, Dugald's uncle Hugh, coming with cattle over the Colintraive ferry, lost them when they took fright at the sound of their own hooves on the wooden pier. He sent a telegram home to Barmolloch: "Cattle retreated, Hugh defeated. Send reinforcements."

Bought in at around £8.10s., the cattle could sometimes fetch double that figure at Falkirk. That was before the deduction of any expenses such as those at the overnight stances.

"They always had their own stances," said Alex. "Usually they might go about twenty miles a day." After coming out at Auchindrain, they more or less followed the lie of the current road to Loch Lomondside. "When you put your cattle into a stance after they had been walking all day, they would lie down. They were tired and did not go far afield."

Beardie dogs—probably brought up in croft kitchens as so many drovers dogs were—were popular among the drovers. "My father told me about someone in a drove in front of him who had a bitch. It was having pups along the route and they kept coming across pups which had been trampled to death. It was a fearful walk if the drive was lasting maybe nine to ten days," added Alex.

The cattle taken by Dugald MacDougall and the MacLellands would have been well tended at Barmolloch before the drives east. Alex recalls that a hundred head of cattle could be wintered there "plus a horse. They cut all the fodder for that number of cattle with the scythe and never bought feed."

Drovers tried to steer clear of severe weather conditions. Alex remembered, however, his father telling him that on one occasion he had to leave a bullock which had foundered at the top of the Rest and Be Thankful beside the Black Spout. The bullock was picked up hale and hearty on the next drive.

Normally the drives, sometimes converging with others coming down from the Oban direction, would arrive two or three days before the Trysts to allow the stock time to condition. On occasions cattle were swum across the lower end of Loch Lomond to shorten the route. For others there was then a ferry crossing from Inverbeg to Rowardennan.

A clap of the hand finalised the deal between seller and buyer at Falkirk. "That was the bargain sealed; and it was as good as suppose it was in a lawyer's book when they struck hands," old Dugald has recalled.

Despite the trudge, Alex said his father enjoyed the job. Perhaps though he did not think so much of it when the combustion engine took over and the mechanised cattle float appeared. When he met the Queen in rain-swept Oban and she asked Dugald why he did not drive cattle any longer—this was in 1956 when he was ninety-one—he replied: "Drive cattle now? The roads aren't fit for man or beast!"

I have also heard some vivid yarns from the late Sandy Mackay whose Gaelic-speaking father took the black cattle from the machairs of Lewis and Harris to the Muir of Ord and Falkirk Trysts. Sandy himself had strode with the droving collies of old on seven-day tramps behind the hoggs of the central country.

He absorbed a lot of knowledge when he watched and listened to his father. "I can remember the old boys droving cattle which had come off the isles and bringing them through this district. My father was at it too for seven years, swimming cattle across from Skye to Lochalsh and taking them to the Trysts.

"I was awfully fond of gossip and I used to listen to my father and other men talking. Mind you, I was always getting a ring across the ear for it."

I first met Sandy when he was seventy-four years old and at work at the Mollands, Callander which he farmed for fifty-one years.

One had to be fit for the droving. Sandy's own experiences at the hogg drives came when he returned from the war and took shepherding jobs whilst his brother looked after the farm.

"In 1926 I had a drove of about 600 hoggs to take from the Killin area away through to Fife for wintering. We went via Dunblane and Glendevon. We would be six days on the road. A big number of hoggs went away through to that district each winter. We had no bother with the traffic—there was the odd motor car but you would not get two together.

"There were usually two of us with the sheep. We had to find our own overnight grass keep on the road and so needed the two men because one went ahead calling at farms to see if we could get the night's keep. It wasn't difficult. Most farmers then helped the sheep men out. They were used to them each year. Some of them took nothing in the way of money. The sheep did not eat much anyway if they had been walked sixteen miles in a day—they just wanted to lie down. If there was one with an ailment we could leave it at the farm until we came back in the spring.

"We always had good dogs. They were good road dogs. They were good hill dogs too but it was a different kind of dog we had in these days. They were the kind which did not need many orders. They would go along the sides of the drove and watch the gates themselves to prevent

17

sheep going through. That was the way to train a dog—on the road with hoggs.

"We never turned the hoggs back if we were meeting a vehicle or some obstacle. If you kept turning them back they got soured and sticky. If you let them draw away on they were not ill to drive at all. Coming back with them in the spring of the year was easy—we didn't really need any help. They seemed to know the way to their own place as if they had walked it before.

"Mostly they were ewe hoggs and I would stay with them during the winter on the Fife farms. Your own personal keep was in along with the price of wintering the hoggs. In these days it would not be more than 4s or 5s a head.

"We would meet in with plenty of other droves on the road but we had no bother keeping the flocks from joining. If we were meeting anything one of us would go into the first gate. We kept away from the towns as much as we could. The kids there were more bother than the traffic."

Some of Sandy's droves lasted well over a week. Which might seem nothing to the plods of his father, Christopher, a drover/crofter from Lochalsh and son of one of the Mackays cleared from sad Strathnaver. Christopher would be one of the last of that old bevy of men for his experiences came near the end of the great droving times.

The old man in fact was only one of seventeen Mackay families who had to leave Strathnaver where I have seen on a raw winter's night the tragic shadows of the clearances.

Sandy's grandfather eventually wandered to Lochalsh. No one would give them shelter on route for fear of reprisals. So he was opposite the misty isle which was to play a big part in Christopher Mackay's droving career. Christopher gathered not only the cattle from Skye, he went further west too, over the waters to Lewis and Harris to bring to the mainland beasts already purchased by Scots cattle dealers.

"Father was seven years at the droving, gathering from all the isles," said Sandy. "This would be about the 1880's when he was still young. What they did not sell at the Muir of Ord Tryst were taken down to Falkirk.

"My father used to say it wasn't a hard life. They got on fine. He did not make money at it. Maybe he was getting £7 for six months and his keep and sometimes gained a tip or two. But he was always meeting old friends and cronies.

"There were some grand cattle dogs coming out of Skye. I remember hearing of one man who used to drove from Skye to Falkirk. He had an awfully good dog. He sold it three times at Falkirk to Englishmen. And every time when he got back to Skye the dog was there before him. So he stopped taking it to Falkirk in case they recognised it at the end.

"I remember too a one-armed drover called McGillivray. He always carried a bag of meal in a haversack and this did himself and his dog if they got stuck for a night's lodgings.

"Mostly the drovers were wearing the old homespun clothes. They had real hill buits. In fact they could never have stood the job with anything else. They were all hand made, and well made. It was reckoned a pair should last a year but they did a tremendous amount of walking. The price of them would not be more then eighteen shillings." Today they probably cost £60.

At the start of a trip, Sandy's father had to swim the cattle across from Skye. "It wasn't so bad if the tide was right," said Sandy. "But the ferryman was in charge. There would be a boat going across in front to get some of the cattle started. There could be as many as 200 beasts and it was very seldom they lost any, unless the current was strong.

"Once they got on the drove roads they were never in a hurry. They grazed and travelled at the same time. About ten or fifteen miles and there would usually be a stance or stopping place and they would meet in with other drovers there."

It is obvious a lot of these stances were at inns and cottages from a look at some of the droving routes. And if drovers were anything like the old fashioned shepherds, it is more than likely that as they trod the mountain realms they would be knitting socks or whittling new sticks.

One of the dealers Sandy's father worked for was a Mr McCrae who regularly had one of the big turnouts at the Falkirk Tryst. Some 50,000 head of cattle, it is said, could change hands in private bargaining between Scots and English dealers in two days at the event. Mostly the Tryst would last three days and sometimes an average of 25,000 sheep also found new owners.

The return journey to the likes of Lochalsh would be a cheery one. "Aye, they would head away back, maybe doing thirty or forty miles a day then," said Sandy.

"There were some grand old drovers on the road then. There would be a company of them and there would be a big spree on the road." Drovers with the mettle of Sandy deserved their epitaphs. This poem was penned in his honour. Alas, I have been unable to identify the author.

The Seasons of Sandy Mackay

Hae ye heard o' a fermer ca'd Sandy Mackay
    Real spruce for his age though his youth is weel by
He's respectit by a' be it colonel or tink
    An' the lady's gey often gie Sandy the wink

He's fond o' a crack wi' his cronies at e'en
    Aboot day's that are gane and the sets they hae seen
An roon his bit ingle aye sooner or later
    Oot frae the drawer comes a drap o' the crater

19

In the spring o' the year he is oot tae the hill
Attendin' his flock wi' baith patience and skill
An' aye at the lambin' the ewes needna fear
When Mackay wi' the pack roon' his shoulder is near

When summer comes roon' and the hey's at its best
For Sandy Mackay there's nae thought o' rest
The reaper works on jist as lang as there's licht
An' langer perhaps if the min's kinna bricht

The autumn, the harvest, an' a' thing forbye
Is nae toil, but a pleasure tae Sandy Mackay
He's a son o' the soil in foul weather or fair
An God help the Mollands if he wisnae there

In chill nichts o' winter when the beasts are a' fed
And weel happit doon wi' clean straw for a bed
Mackay will dress up and gang jountenly doon
Tae a ball in the Ancaster, Dreadnought or Croon

Like maist o' the fermers Mackay's no tee-total
And whiles he'll indulge in a drap frae the bottle
But that's no a fault for a Scotsman that's dry
And a' Scots tae the backbone is Sandy Mackay

In summer or winter, springtime or fall
A call at the Mollands is remembered by all
So here's a toast ere the bottle runs dry
May auld Nick be lang dead afore Sandy Mackay

Another old drover I have met, Bob Wilson, who would tramp with wintering hoggs from Jedburgh to Newcastle got eight bob a day for it. Three score Half-bred hoggs penned outside an overnight stance and whisky at three shillings a bottle at the inn with the beer at three ha'pence a pint—that was part of his life.

"Aye, it was threepence an ounce for baccy with a clay pipe and a box of matches thrown in with it," recalled Bob when I had a crack with him in 1974. Which sounds a satisfying life until he adds that his daily wage on the five-day sixty-five-mile tramp in charge of feeding and ewe hoggs was only eight shillings and from that had to be deducted the cost of the lodgings.

"It was a good job for a lad, seeing a bit of life," added Bob—he was eighty-six when I met him—recalling the days between 1904 and 1914 when three or four times a year he took to the droving with his two collies and a mate.

He was one of the last surviving drovers of that area in the Borderland who could speak with experience of the trek over Carter Bar, by Catcleugh, along the Rede, over the commons of Otterburn steering the hoggs to dairy pastures around Seaton Burn, Ponteland and Gosforth.

Bob had taken to the droving—when his casual freelance shepherding work allowed—when he was sixteen years old and his drives to Northumberland were with stock belonging to the Misses Barrie who farmed Harden Mains.

Some 600 feeding hoggs were driven down the road in August and brought back in October to the turnips at Harden Mains. And 600 ewes were taken down to winter until March or April. In addition to his charges he had sometimes forty to fifty cattle bought for Harden Mains at Hexham or Ponteland.

"We could cover the sixty-five miles in five days with the hoggs," said Bob, who was accompanied by another shepherd. "We just took the main road over Carter. We stopped the first night at Whitelee on the other side of the Border near the reservoir, the second night at the Redesdale Arms, the third night near Kirkwhelpington and the last night on the north side of Ponteland."

At the end of their daily mileage they mostly put up at farmhouses with the hoggs penned outside. Apart from that one night on each trip at the Redesdale Arms.

"We had to take a change of clothes with us for the weather could be bad. What we wore was first class working clothes and my hand-made boots would cost perhaps £1.

"We always got a piece made up in the mornings at the places where we stopped and that kept us going through the day, although if there was a shop on the way we might buy something. We got away at daylight with the hoggs. In the summer time we let them feed during the day along the side of the road because at nights they were shut in the pens. In the spring when we were bringing the hoggs back we could put them in the fields at night. That did not cost anything because there was no grass there for them to eat anyway. We enjoyed the work—we did not know better."

For two winters Bob stayed down in the Newcastle area with the sheep at £1 a week, minus eleven shillings for lodgings "so when you had baccy and beer paid there was not much left."

After First World War service Bob spent twenty-one years as shepherd at Oxnam Neuk and had another thirty years at Oxnam Row where he lived when I met him. This included twelve years on the outbye Bloodylaws hirsel.

Another character with droving experience whom I recall meeting in 1972 was Peter Brown, then a gleg ninety-two who had been a shepherd all his life and had taken part in seventy-three lambings. In that time he had only missed ten days through illness.

He had started lambing at nine years of age and began full time shepherding at The Lurg, Fintry at fourteen with "a wee bundle under my oxter and an' auld dug at ma fit."

He had drives with hoggs to winter in the Stirling area. "I remember once there were two of us bringing 900 ewes back in one lot. The first ones went on themselves, wanting to get back to the hill, and they were back on the farm two hours before the leaders of the main bunch. They took the right direction at the crossroads."

Once a jovial policeman jocularly told Peter when droving a big flock: "I'm going to report you for obstruction." There would not be any kind of motorised vehicle for twenty miles.

Peter could recall some cattle droving too. "I remember taking some wild Highland cattle to Stirling market—about fifteen pedigree heifers which had never been off the hills. But I had a grand old dog which would tackle anything. That morning there was a thick mist. I could only hear them clattering along in front. We went over the moor and on to the old road and the only thing I could hear was their coughing. But we got right through Stirling before there was a soul up in the morning."

Peter left the hills for lowground sheep at Kinaldy near St Andrews where I met him, in his retirement.

Today many of the old drove roads are once again being discovered and utilised by hikers and horse riders who are finding pleasure in the footsteps of these legendary figures.

POET OF THE HIDDEN GLEN

For fifty years John Dickson was a shepherd. Most of his time was spent in a lonesome glen in Tweedsmuir, itself a quiet area in Scotland's Southern Uplands. John Dickson was to become a much-loved folk-poet telling vividly of his times and rural life. I took to his paths once and talked with some of those who had known him.

When the cottar folks in the burnhead dwellings watch the ewes seeking their dykeback bield or foregathering near the stells, then winter's sting has come to the hill glens.

It will come again to the changing valley of Tweedsmuir. So will the onward march of the trees, creeping stealthily over the bentgrass, suffocating the heritage of bygone times when the hill dwellers gave it all a purpose.

Maybe it will not all be lost. There is still by the burnsides of the Menzion, the Fruid, the Hearthstane and the Polmood, a leftover chapter to be written in Scotland's pastoral history. And in the hushed glen of Stanhope, a hidden outbye world of its own, lie the very seeds of the yarn that may one day be told.

Those who have been abroad in Stanhope glen on an autumn day cannot but be impressed with its serenity. From the heights of Dollar Law, where the Stone Grain runs down to Stanhope burn and beside Glentinning burn on the other side, the pastel dark colours breed a calmness broken only by the striking rowan trees.

I have walked this glen, below the loose scree of Craig Head. Past Taberon Law up the burnsides to the foot of Dollar Law. Following the footsteps of a much-loved man whose words, born within him as he tended Blackfaces on this lonely high ground and put on scraps of wrapping paper when he returned to his cote home, have brought inspiration and enjoyment to many who, then and now, follow his calling—that of the hill shepherd.

John Dickson, who was born in back-aboot herding country in Galloway and wrought for forty-two years at Stanhope, made the history of this sheep land around Tweedsmuir and Drumelzier much richer and homelier through his wisdom penned in verse and in talks at gatherings of sheepmen. But such as John Dickson, known for many years to readers of *The Scottish Farmer* as 'Hill Herd' and to other readers as 'Border Herd' are now very few. The folk-poets breathing the very tang of the bog myrtle, the keb-hoose, the high sheep pads or the rural howff are a vanished race.

John Dickson's death in the early 1960's left a gap which will never be filled. There are too few left now—John Byers, another herding poet known as 'Blue Bell' with whom I used to crack in his Newcastleton home died in 1967—to hand down the lore of the past.

'Hill Herd' summed up his chores thus:

"I'm a herd frae Stanhope in Peebleshire. My hirsel rins frae the haughs on the side o' the Tweed, tae the tap o' Dollar Law, amang the highest points in the sooth o' Scotland.

"The view ye get frae its toorin height, at fower o'clock on a gatherin' mornin' could hardly be bate. Y're lookin' richt ower the Yarrow and Ettrick, tae the Cheviot Hills. In fact, the hale Border country is in view, forbye the grey hills o' Galloway and Heilan' Peaks ayont my ken. The heichts o' Blackhouse are quite near, where Hogg, the Ettrick Shepherd, tentit his flock in days gane by.

"Mony chinges hae taen place since Hogg's day, but a 'herd's wark gangs on juist aboot the same. Lang faces wi' bad lammin's, and thrang days wi' clippin's, dippin's and speanin's."

Born into a herding family at the head of the Water of Deugh in the Carsphairn region of Galloway in 1886—this glen is now completely timbered—John Dickson was to become in his Stanhope days a fresh, homely, informative and knowledgeable observer of hill farm life. Mainly through his verses he passed this on for his fellow men in the glens and hills.

In all he would herd for fifty years. Some forty-two of these were at Stanhope. "Wud I have stuck to it a' these years if I hadna liked it?" he would say.

His herding days began in Dumfriesshire when he was thirteen after schooling around Penpont village. His first wage was £7 for a term, for in these days youngsters helped a shepherd in the summer time with sheep work, hay and peat. His first sole charge was at Beoch in Ayrshire tending sixteen score of ewes with a wage rising from £16 to £20 a year. He also tried the Trossachs but had a short stay—"its nae guid for hill sheep at a', the scenery is the best thing aboot the place."

So it was back again to the Blackface country around Muirkirk and Afton. And in 1909 he came to Stanhope, first to the outbye Hope hirsel where he herded for ten years before moving to the east side hefts. In his forty-two years at the farm he served five masters—"I was just taen ower wi' the sheep," he quipped.

He found changes at Stanhope from his boyhood days and described them thus:

> The langer that I tramp the steep
> Auld Blackface ewes amang
> It seems to me in breeding sheep
> There's something far gaen wrang

24

In fancy's e'e, I still can see
The kind that used to graze
In days lang gaen, when I was wee
On Deuch and Euchan's braes

Yon sheep grew wool, where wool should be
Had noble heads and frames
A wild and hardy glinting e'e
And thick and cleanly banes

They took the brae at break o' day
Through sunshine, snaw or storm
And didna' stand and look for hay
Or 'herds wi' pokes o' corn

But, strange to say, e'en men o' sense
Beguiled wi fashion's charm
Were led astray at much expense
To work so muckle harm

They fostered silly hot-house freaks
Clad ower wi horselike hair
Wi' muff aroun' their legs and cheeks
Wi' hurchins best compare

Their lambs they widna even sook
A' natural instincts gane
They, like their sires, prefer to jeuk
Aroun' some ingle stane

But what's the use of Scotland's crests
Unless we've got the breed
To stan' in natural covering dres't
On heath and bent to feed?

May saner judgement soon prevail
'Mang men of Blackface lore
And breed us something in the vale
Like what they had of yore

Married on £40 a year, John Dickson's salary when he moved down Stanhope glen to the east side cottage was augmented by a cow, a free load of meal, a thousand yards of potatoes and two sheep.

He called the east side a "sair hirsel." These words were also used by shepherd William Lawrie who, when I wrote a feature on John Dickson in the winter of 1968, took the same pad after his breakfast as the hill poet took in his former days. "It *is* a sair herding but not as bad as some," William told me. "There is a lot of rough scree to start with but it is easier on top."

William, then fourteen years at Stanhope which was being farmed by the Animal Breeding Research Organisation, used to herd Mossfennan and Drumelzier Haugh. On the latter he marched or neighboured with Stanhope's east side and on an odd occasion would meet John Dickson on the hill. "He was a grand cracker about folk without criticising them," recalled William.

John Dickson's road to the hill in the morning began with a steep climb up a pad at the back of the little cottage. "When he was old he would look up the hill and say 'No wonder my legs are done,' said his daughter Mrs Jardine Troughton who was born at Stanhope and whom I talked with in her Biggar home.

From the top of the first climb there was a six-mile tramp away out to Dollar Law at the far end of the 1,500-acre hirsel—maybe a four-hour stint if conditions were good, for this six foot tall shepherd who tended 500-plus ewes. He did not skimp his duties.

"Ony ideas that I hae aboot sheep I got them wi' gaun among them, so if I am a lang road off the mark you'll ken no tae blame ony special professor," he once said.

"Gaun among" the sheep at his everyday shepherding, wearing a balaclava over his bonnet in snowstorms, brought the inspiration which John Dickson put into his poems, some of which were published in book form.

Mrs Troughton told me: "He made most of his poetry up in his mind while on the hill. In these days we saved up all the paper wrappings. He would come in from the hill, ask for some paper and then scribble down a poem before having his dinner. He would read it to my mother and ask her what she thought of it, and then write it over again on better paper."

He was very close to nature, as indeed all shepherds are, and in his poem "Auld Scotland's Heather-Bell" he includes these verses:

When storms severe, or winter's frost
  All nature's plants benumb
The fancy flowers, that pounds have cost
  May wither and succumb
But you, from out your mossy bed
  Be winter calm or snell
Aye spread again your carpet red
  My dear wee heather-bell
You need no artificial heat
  Nor frames around thee laid
By gardeners who in turn compete
  With graip, and hoe, or spade
But wrapped where lonely shepherds reign
  And grouse and laverocks dwell
You sleep until you're due again
  Wee hardy heather-bell

26

At the many shepherds' suppers at which John Dickson spoke, his talks were always in broad Scots. His pawkiness delighted any company. He told, for instance at one supper about the two 'herds wives discussing the lambing season together.

"Hoo's yer man getting on?" asked one of the other. "Weel, he's no sayin' onything . . . but he's flingin' the furniture aboot, an' I doot its no' a guid sign" was the reply.

"My father was just a very old type of shepherd—interested in his work," said Mrs Troughton. "He had no desire to do anything else." And from many others whom I talked to about 'Hill Herd' came the same reply. Although he might have made a name for himself in other professions he had no wish to exchange his calling.

His forebears were shepherds, with descent from Renwick the Covenanter, and in the company of the peewits, the whaups, his collies and the Blackfaces on Stanhope, he had time for little else.

He once said shepherds could not be directed—nobody knew where to direct them. Their working hours knew no limit; sometimes they worked all day and through the night as well. 'Herding was a solitary occupation, but the fact that he was a long way from the 'pictures' or football matches never worried the right kind of man.

Speaking once at St Mary's 'Herd's supper on tendencies of this mechanised age, John Dickson said he had never seen a 'herd made in a blacksmith's shop—"a combine to dae a' that a 'herd has tae dae wud be a gey intricate machine."

And in what must be one of his best poems, "The Auld Mill Wheel" he had more to say of progress:

Auld wheel, you noo in ruins lie
　　Beside the Stanhope burn
Wha's waters, in the days gane bye
　　Hae gien you mony a turn.
You were a relic o' the past
　　To gie us corn and meal
But noo, I doot, you've turned your last
　　The Auld Mill Wheel

For near a hunner year you stood
　　Against the auld barn wa'
And tempests wild you hae withstood
　　O' wun and rain and snaw
But noo a turbine's in your place
　　A dynamo as weel
And you seem lying in disgrace
　　The Auld Mill Wheel

27

But auld freen, dinna think o' shame
   You nobly did your bit
And they, wha noo your place hae taen
   Are maybe no sae fit
Altho' the eye they seem to please
   They're scraps of iron and steel
Lang, lang afore they've run your lease
   The Auld Mill Wheel

But noo the cry is a' for speed
   Its hurry, hurry on
And even folk, wi' selfish greed
   Wad trample ithers doon
But whether this is richt, or wrang
   Or for auld Scotland's weal
I grudge the road you had to gang
   The Auld Mill Wheel

On you the artists looked wi' pride
   I've watched them in the glen
Sae quietly by the burnie side
   Applying brush and pen
On you to hand you doon to fame
   Could I but dae as weel
In writing this, to praise thy name
   The Auld Mill Wheel

Such backward looks, beside the burn
   Awaken in my min'
A thocht, it's comin on our turn
   To share like fate, as thine
For after a' the great and sma'
   To nature's voice maun kneel
Let's hope our record is as braw
   As thine, Auld Mill Wheel

So the Auld Wheel went silent. So too did the old drove roads through Tweedsmuir. John Dickson knew them well. Many a time he drove his Blackface sheep from Stanhope to the market at Lanark and several times to Peebles.

He took an old road by way of Broughton and Skirling and would rest the night at Warrenhill. One year for some reason he changed the field where the sheep were enclosed for the night. It meant going past the field he was in the habit of using—and his collie just would not do this.

John Dickson had strong views on collies, especially the ones competing at sheepdog trials. It is an age old argument.

"There is plenty of folk that uphaud the pampering of the sheep, but still they are awful down on the dog trials," he said. "I put them baith in the same category. You see the best of them on the day of the exhibition but thae hae baith been quite successful.

"The sheep men had the feeding for their ideal for making good sheep and they hae managed to breed a race of sheep that will not do without it. The dog men's ideal was command, and they hae bred a race of dogs that just need to be commanded, but if either of them hae improved the stock frae a 'herd's point of view, this is not the 'herd that can see it.

"A wheen toon's folk, or millionaires, think it is great work to see a man with twa dogs on a golf course that can keep ane lying, and the ither ane running. But take the same two dogs on to a hirsel of 2,000 acres, the ae half stanes and the ither half brackens to hunt up fifty mawked sheep in one day . . . it might be a worse job to keep ane running the time the ither ane was lying."

His comments on the sheepdog trials collies brought plenty of response in the papers. Replying once to a writer signing himself "Old School' John Dickson responded:

> If trial dogs are what you say
>   Why no' gie them the work to dae
> It seems so queer that dogs o' fame
>   Aye dae sae little work at hame
>
> Now, as you say, I understand
>   A dog must be in fair command
> But here as well, I'd like to state
>   At times the word we over-rate
>
> At trials you hae seen, I hope
>   Some dogs their master couldna' stop
> While others stoppit like a dart—
>   but then, again, they wadna start
>
> Then others still will come like reek
>   But can't be trusted near the sheep
> So I would say, they're scarce the breed
>   To trust while daily work we need
>
> But trial dogs I'll leave them noo
>   They're just the same's the showyard coo
> She chews her cud in sweet content
>   While others slave to pay the rent

But 'Hill Herd' had respect for the trials men too. In a poem he sent to the legendary Jim Wilson of Innerleithen—'J.M.'—on winning the International Sheepdog Trials championship shield outright in 1934, John Dickson wrote:

Baith Bruce and Wallace, Scotland boast
Wha stemmed the prood invading host
And Burns' talent ne'er was crossed
    Despite his follies
But Wilson's name noo tops the toast
    For trials collies.

In the same poem he put in a word for his own collies:

I've haen some fairish dogs mysel
Far distant heights they'd rin them well
Or wild, determined bleaters quell
    'Mang moorland scenes
But yours the surging crowd can swell
    Mid Kings and Queens

John Dickson usually went out to his hefts on the east side of Stanhope with two collies, or one if he was training a pup. It was hard ground and he always parted with his dogs at about five or six years old.

One, old Jed, was sold into the Muirkirk area where John had once herded himself. He put Jed on the train at Broughton—but the collie wandered back to Stanhope Glen within a week.

A gathering or a clipping brought together countless collies and a big collection of 'herds who neighboured for such events. John Dickson enjoyed this neighbouring and his daughter told me she had seen more than twenty men at a Stanhope clipping in her childhood days.

Such foregatherings always meant John getting called on for a poem or a talk. Many times it would be about the sheep he tended. And no doubt many times too he sunk the image of the 'hoose-fed' sheep—those pampered inside buildings so that they looked in better fettle for the sales or shows.

"What I ca' a hill sheep" he once said "is ane that needs nae decoration and can tend for itself summer and winter unless completely blocked wi' snaw and frost." And what did he like to see in his sheep? "The main ideal for years back has been a great big head—ae thing I am quite shair is hereditary, if nocht else is, for their fathers was often cabbage fed and like the cabbage's ain head, its at its best in October, but it'll no stand the winter. The warst thing about yon heids, they are maistly abune their mooth, and the lower jaw where the teeth are is like to disappear altogether.

"The hindquarters are another thing that hae been badly sacrificed for the fancy head and they are what I consider the best point in ony sheep. I never saw ane that had guid gigots and four guid legs tae gaun on but what had a quite faceable heid to gang on a hill wi'.

30

"My opinion of a hill ewe is that if she is not a good one on her ain heft on the hill, it does not matter where you take her or what you feed her on, or how you dress her, you canna make her a better hill sheep. You may improve the look of her, but she is aye going farer frae her trade and so is anything she is likely to breed."

It was even better in 'Hill Herd's' verses:

> Nae doot in far back lambing days
> The herds gaed whistling up the braes
> Maist every lamb that met their gaze
> Was sookit fu'
> Lord, bliss my stars, compare the phrase
> To what it's noo.
>
> Each second herd that takes the hill
> Is armed wi' instrument or pill
> For dysentry or loupin-ill
> Or some disease
> And still you say the 'pampered rule'
> Excels with ease.

Still on the vaccines, John Dickson had a look at what young shepherds going into the profession could expect. "Some folk say oor grandfaithers wadna think much of the young 'herds nooadays. That's maybe richt, but the young ones will get on better among the sheep noo than their grandfaithers wad dae. They wadna ken where tae start among bottles and syringes and pills. In my young days there was only yin bottle and it cured baith the 'herd and the sheep."

Talking to people who knew John Dickson, I heard the tale of a visit he paid to the Biggar Show. Wandering along to the Blackface ring he gazed solemnly for a while at flockmasters and herds dressing the sheep with sticks and brushes and the wool lying on the ground. "What's going on," he queried a spectator, "is it a clippin' or a dog hunt?"

The cote in Stanhope Glen where John Dickson lived for ten years has long lain empty. When I have been over part of the east side hirsel where he herded for his different masters, I could see in this little glen where he got the inspiration for his poems and talks. Under the name of 'Border Herd' he wrote for twenty-five years in the *Southern Reporter* one of the best pastoral weeklies.

Mr William Wilson was Editor then. "John had the happy knack of being able to make friends and possibly even more important, to keep friends. He had a droll sense of humour without being flamboyant about it," Mr Wilson said.

When John Dickson retired to Biggar, Mr Wilson was a regular visitor. "His room was typical of a shepherd. He had family portraits and showed me his long service medal. But what struck me always was his welcome

31

smile and at all times I remember his firm and sincere handshake."

To Mr Wilson, John Dickson was 'Border Herd.' To Mr Tom Dickson he was 'Uncle Jake.' "I often met him at shows and sales," Tom told me at his retirement home in Durisdeer, Dumfriesshire. Tom had then retired from a herding life which began at Mair, Carsphairn (where his uncle was born) and later New Cumnock, Crawfordjohn and Sanquhar.

"I remember two events which I attended with him. One was when he gave a lecture at Closeburn when a Young Farmers Club was being formed. Then he was Chairman at the New Cumnock 'Herds supper. He was a good speaker. It was not easy to trip him up—he aye was ready with an answer."

'Hill Herd' had indeed an answer ready when the authorities decided to close some country schools:

> They've shairly little in their heids
>   Wha canna see it plain
> That what our country sairly needs
>   Is land re-stocked again
>
> There's nocht aroun' but idle ploos
>   And places gaun to wreck
> Within the kirks, the empty pews
>   Where our forefathers met
>
> They pay our 'dole' while unemployed
>   Stan haudin up hoose ens
> When needful work might be enjoyed
>   Within our moorland glens
>
> They've taxed the land beyond remead
>   And brocht us to our doom
> But built some fancy schules insteid
>   To learn the weans to soom
>
> Then thousands mair on motors gang
>   To drive them there and back
> Wha wad be better learned alang
>   The paths they mean to walk
>
> May common sense at length prevail
>   And stem the townward tide
> Until yince mair o'er hill and dale
>   We see our needs supplied
>
> For after a' is said and done
>   A' maist in every nation
> The men who highest laurels won
>   Had self-learned education

32

In an area not far from where James Hogg, the Ettrick Shepherd, has penned in memorable words vivid details of mighty storms, John Dickson too had some unnerving experiences. Tom Dickson remembered his uncle speaking of lambing time in 1919. "It would be April 27th. It was a good day when they went away to the hill. There would be a score or more ewes with lambs in the meadow. When they came back at night there was not one to be seen." They were buried in snow.

There must have been a bad one in 1937 at Stanhope. For next year 'Hill Herd' described it: "The maist dangerous time o' a' for baith the herds and the sheep are snawstorms o' winter. We had twae bad anes last year, ane in March when a gey wheen sheep were happit and anither in December that wrocht some mischief as weel. Of course, nane o' them could compare wi' the Gonial Blast in 1794 when seventeen herds and hunners o' sheep were washed intae the Solway when the thow cam.' "

In the same talk he added this little homily: "Herds are no' very thrang the noo, but the time's comin' again when we'll no get muckle peace frae daylicht tae dark."

But John Dickson was always 'weel happit' himself for the snow. Like many shepherds of the day he was a knitter. Not only did he knit his own Balaclavas and his own socks but he also knitted for relatives and friends.

The knitting ran in the family. His brother William, who herded a long spell on the in-bye ground at Stanhope, was known to take the knitting with him to his sheep ground and could click a fair stitch or two when hunting out his collies.

'Hill Herd' was a faithful chronicler of how conditions changed in the hill glens. History could be grateful for this. For example:

> They drive our weans to school in motors
>> Instead of slates, they've fancy jotters
> Although in debt, the country sotters
>> Some million dollars
> But does it make them surer voters
>> Or better scholars.
>
> We noo are seeing great inventions
>> Far yont our forebears' comprehensions
> Transports and ships of great dimensions
>> And aeroplanes
> And wireless sets, wi' good intentions
>> But fact remains—
> What odds will't make how high folk flee
>> Or what the tourist's speed may be
> Or yet how deep within the sea
>> Their engines boil
> If none a helping hand will gie
>> To till the soil?

There was sometimes sadness too. In the last article he wrote while in hospital, John Dickson said: "Times and customs have changed rapidly this century and few women can see the charms of such isolated places (the upland glens) and naturally the men will not go without them, with the result many former homesteads are only marked by gable-ends, the rest being overgrown with nettle, rashes or brackens."

Even then he had time to think back on the lore of the world which he graced for more than seventy-seven years. "Kenning sheep is a great gift, not necessarily hereditary. Some folk imagine that is all a herd needs to make him a reliable man, but the sheep he kens so well will get covered with mawks or dee coupit if he does not attend to them; exactly the same as with a man who does not ken them.

"A minister was once passing a few boys where one of them was swearing very bad. He went up to the boy and asked him who in the world learned him to swear like that. 'Oh man, the boy replied, 'it's a thing you will never learn richt, its a gift.' No doubt kennin' sheep and even folk, is the same."

With his poet's eye, the shepherd John Dickson portrayed what could be a vanishing part of Scotland's heritage. But he envied none. Or, as he put it himself:

> Roads whiles may seem lanesome and braes unco steep
> For wi' fate's dire decision we're forced to compete
> But the lot of the shepherd who wanders alone
> Is whiles to be envied by Kings on the throne

These are the words of a hill shepherd—the wisest of men. It would be a pity if they were forgotten.

THE LONG GATHER

On the tourist road to the west at Cairndow between Arrochar and Inverary lie high sheep rakes, long respected by all sheepmen. To be a shepherd on these towering mountains was to be guardian of one of the most rugged and hard sheep tendings in the country. The Noble family's estates there held an annual sale in one of the farmstead sheds and drew a big turnout of buyers and spectators. Preparation for the sale stretched into weeks. I went with the shepherds of Cairndow on one of their gathers for the sale before shepherds and sheep left this land in the late 1970's to make way for trees on a big acreage.

About three hours after a ton of collies had been loosed in a flurry of freedom at the mountain bottom, the glen-side began to bleed white. Another day in the Cairndow gather was well under way.

Where scores of burns came splattering through gully and bracken down to the tourist route west, between 650 and 700 Blackfaces were steered in a river to the glen floor, ringed by hill men and their dogs. Nine men, maybe thirty-odd collies.

Ernie MacPherson and Archie Campbell had cleaned the tops of sheep at the back of the mountains. Old hand Jimmy Waddell and Donald Beaton had taken some of the weight of the ever-enlarging flock along the bottom. Between them, coming from either side, seven others with brown dog, blue merle, beardie and hunter had tidied up the face and the rocks, leaving Lechdain's three mile stretch denuded of stock. Well, almost.

"A comfortable day," head shepherd Donald MacPherson said as the sea of white was marshalled in the Butterbridge pens at the top end of Glen Kinglas while holiday trippers slowed or stopped to see the work. "It is not always such plain sailing," added Donald who had then been forty-three years on this ground between the head of the Rest and Be Thankful and the River Fyne.

There can be trials and toils before the eleven hirsels on Cairndow yield their crop for the annual sale in the Achadunan farm shed. Cairndow's mighty spread, at that time covering around 22,000 acres and stocked with three to four thousand breeding ewes, could be gathered in thirteen days for the sale—held jointly with neighbouring Ardkinglas—if all went well.

This was far from being guaranteed. There are mists which can curl into the glen and frustratingly hang around for days or weeks or just come and go. Men can be on some of the 3,000 ft high tops and look down on it. Useless gathering weather.

"I've seen it only two days before the sale when we got the last of the stock in," said Donald MacPherson, whose team of nine shepherds on the Cairndow estate of Lord Glenkinglas finished up with several thousand Blackface and cross lambs annually for the sale along with some of the older draft ewes.

Thirteen days could do for Cairndow's gather in these peak times. But mostly it could be anything up to six weeks before all the lambs were eventually gathered, drawn and put in the lowground fields beside the River Fyne to await sale day.

A hirsel a day was good going. There were six on the Achadunan side of the estate and another five on Ardno where Donald's son Ernie was head shepherd. If pushed, the cheery squad could hie out and take in two hirsels a day.

The toughest they covered meant five or six hours on the mountains before parking a thousand head of ewes and lambs into the fanks. That was from the ground on top of the Rest on Lechain hirsel, tricky territory of rocks and corries and 600 ewes. "It was not bad if you knew the territory," said Donald. "Mind you, it is a lovely sight to see all the ewes and lambs going in. We do not appreciate it ourselves but the tourists were there with their cameras flying."

They were there when we finished the gather one day in 1977 on Lechdain, the steep stretch on the north side of the Glen, topped by Binnein An Fhileir and scuds of dreaded mist. Since then much of the land has gone into forestry and many of the shepherds I walked with—and a big percentage of the sheep—have gone.

Three hours before the sheep were finally penned that 1977 day we had disgorged from a Land Rover and horse box which was weighed down by man and dog so much it was difficult to steer. Thirty collies suddenly loosed together means freedom and bedlam unlimited. And at that stage all answering everyday names.

Ernie MacPherson whose own hirsel is the Stobb on the south side of the Glen, lit off for the top with four dogs including his hunter—a barking type of sheepdog—called Cora. There is a different atmosphere up there on the very heights, said the Cairndow 'herds. You can stride for miles and miles without a falter. Just so, but only after a stiff climb.

That worthy, Kit Reid on his own ground, fitted in below Ernie, combing the high pads with one of the country's most colourful dog squads including blue-merles Cora and Corrie and the grey Rock on his first-ever gather and A.W.O.L. at the end of it. He would come back no doubt later that day. Kit had with him too, as well as these Skye-blooded rarities, the tough red beardie collie Rhuardh with the blood of Mull. The hunters have value untold on days like that on the upper rims of rock, scree and gully.

Johnstone Munro was below Kit, shod with a handful of dogs from his Scoultain ground and John Baker, enjoying himself on the steep after

36

his normal low ground work on the cross sheep and shed beasts, lit Tweed, Bess and the raffle dog Jock—he was the first prize at a presentation function celebrating the winning of the International Sheep Dog Trials Championship by John Murray—up and down, always on the alert for the animal world's most clever and cussed member, the hill ewe.

Below us was the gaffer, Donald MacPherson, heeled by Jim, Queen, Mirk and Glen and farther down at the fence back was his companion for so many years at Cairndow, Jimmy Waddell with a red dog and a hunter among his tackle. Boasting too a new line in shepherds' crooks—a carpet sweeper shank! However, whatever comes to hand suffices. Nineteen years on the estate and figuring in many gathers Jimmy said: "Sometimes it is worse at the bottom of the hill for you get all the odd sheep landing there."

From the other side of the mountain, out of sight during most of the gather, another three 'herds had started out.

Archie Campbell from Glenkinglas hirsel gathered in the outbye and rocks with his hunter Jack and also Meg and Garry, meeting in with Ernie MacPherson high above Butterbridge. Andy Wilson, who then tended to that rocky airt on Beinn Lochain, commanding Kyle and Nell, was just below him and under that was Donald Beaton, normally on Benachorian and the tall Ben Vane. He had a fair bevy of dogs with him as he helped the East side team tuck in the mountain at that end.

Most 'herds follow the same pads at each of the gathers. So they know how the sheep run.

Did I say they were cussed? Maybe it is wisdom. The old girls, who have been through it all before, look for escape routes. So these barking dogs get ready up top. They are possibly the only thing able to hunt the stock out amongst the rocks. Down below, Jimmy's brown dog was proving useful and already a 'rough'—a sheep missed at shearing time and still sporting her wool—was spotted. Sheep were running well with few twisting back in the relaxed, canny drive.

Way down at ground level, far away across Loch Fyne, Inveraray made a fine picture. So too did the many burns disgorging themselves down the amazingly deep gullies and corries. It wasn't just the dogs which lapped at their fresh water—though mind you, I had been told there was something else in one of these springs. I still haven't found it.

We had to leave one bissom and her lamb perched on a precarious overhang above a corrie. Shepherds on Cairndow have many tales to tell of the fatalities of sheep and dogs over the rocks and down the splits. It would have been foolish to dog this pair and maybe add to the statistics.

Sheep were running easily off the tops, through the occasional skiffs of thick mist which must have been frustrating for the unseen men up there with their barking dogs.

The weight of the ever-gathering stock was beginning to be shoved further down past John to Donald. Some corries were showing their teeth.

The odd ewe and her lamb were keen to sneak into a hide. Here a wrong move by a dog could have been disastrous in the line-up of burns straggling off the mountain side like frayed binder twine.

So canniness was the word all along giving the Blackies their own time to cross. Ernie MacPherson's Roy was tried on a long run back to seek some which had been missed by the cautious sweep. A hind and her calf appeared above the badger setts and curled back between John Baker and Johnstone Munro.

Archie Campbell's red dog was now heard and seen among the rocks in the sky as the men who had started in the west gradually met in with the East-siders. High, so high up, a ewe and her lamb were dislodged from the severe rock country. At the bottom Donald MacPherson had a big bulk of stock now. Bracken was thicker. "In the old days in four foot of bracken, dogs would go up on their legs and start looking for sheep. But there are few hunters now and the good hill dog is very near extinct," said Donald. "It is all this breeding with strong-eyed dogs that has caused it. There is nothing surer. I don't criticise the strong-eyed ones but if you are on the side of a hill with four or five hundred sheep and you have two keekers, you are in a bad way."

So the jokes go on. In fact I was invited that night to a ceilidh being held in the farm shed. "But the official sale is not until next week and it's the night of the sale you hold your famous ceilidh," I said. "Och aye," quipped one of the wags on the long gather. "Aye, next week is the big ceilidh sure enough and a great ceilidh it is. But we have also a ceilidh tonight to practise for it!"

Near the top end, John Baker's outfit, having crossed another gully, spot a ewe and lamb hiding in a burn. They are flushed out. So we came down to Butterbridge and its fanks, a pincer movement of white, pushed into the pens for the drawing, dipping and dosing. The ewes would be turned back to the heights and the lambs taken by cattle float to Achadunan to await the sale.

Another gathering ended. The team headed back by Land Rover to base for dinner.

Lechdain, three miles long and carefully combed for three hours looked strange. Clean and naked of sheep. Just as the men passed a deepish gully, an old ewe and her lamb appeared defiantly, stepping out from their hide-out. Damn!

THE MILL TRAINS

They were sometimes called the mechanical centipedes—the lengthy threshing mill units which travelled all rural roads during the winter months to park in farm stackyards late at nights. By daybreak they had been readied to thresh the oat and wheat stacks to provide animal feed and fodder. The characterless combine harvester now does a job which once brought together twenty to thirty people.

The glens and farm loanings will never again throb to the sounds of the travelling threshing mill nor will the rural air carry their distinctive smells. The millmen are extinct too.

Those who have never smelt the proud tang of a millman's clothing as he came in for breakfast on a threshing morning have missed an essential part of life.

They were heroes in knotted neckerchiefs, greasy bonnets and with pockets long shredded with overstrain through a conglomeration of spanners and stuffed with endless cloths awash in engine oil. Always there was that magic taint and fusion of grease, chaff and oil. Plus more gossip and news of the surrounding countryside than any local newspaper could ever muster.

Apprenticed myself in boyhood times to the cheery mill days, the attraction was a day off school for the pleasure of being choked with dust and oat chaff, a combination which makes a Saharan dust storm seem like a Sunday breeze in the Hebrides. We envied the teams who hauled their mills from August to May around the byways and parked their lengthy tackle in stackyards and fields for the necessary work beside the oat ricks, providing the farmstead with feed, fodder and bedding for the stock wintering.

There are still those who can sniff the tang of the old 'steamers'—the Burrells, the Clayton and Shuttleworths, the Rustons and the Fowlers. I have listened enthralled to Joe Coulthart, a skilled craftsman bordering maybe on the legendary for his stackyard and backroad manoeuvring of a twenty-ton outfit three times the length of a bus.

First tied to the world of chaff and knives when he was fourteen years old—for an old-time guinea a week as his pay—and for decades to guide with care over Kirkcudbrightshire at 7 m.p.h. one of the coal-consuming mill trains which needed water every eight miles or so, Joe was famed along much of Solwayside for his past deeds. He was among the elite of millmen.

Dressed sometimes with clothing which included straw-filled clogs and newspapers wrapped round his chest for insulation on the Burrell traction engine, Joe and his team taking the mighty threshing tackle to the Stewartry's outbye corn ground, have no equal now.

The farmers in these days of the 1920's and 1930's did not ask their corn merchant when they could get the mill. They queried: "When can I get Joe?"

Long retired after forty-five years with the feeds firm of James Wyllie and Sons Ltd., Joe was *the* millman from the Solway shore at scenic Balcary Bay up through the hamlets of Auchencairn, Dundrennan, Borgue, Laurieston, Balmaclellan, Corsock, back round to Castle Douglas, Haugh of Urr and Crocketford. These are the villages and townships. But Joe can recite the farm names and also the roadside burns where his old Burrell steam engine—one of the 'steamers' based at Wyllies' Dumfries mill—had to halt for water.

Joe started with the rival firm of Charltons in Dumfries as a fourteen-year-old. As 'third man' he was mostly forking straw bunches coming off the back of the baler and hauling them to storage sheds. He had also to keep oiling the mechanism for bunching the straw, see that there was a continuous supply of string to tie the bunches and carry out many other menial but essential tasks. It was part of the millmen's organised teamwork.

But the mill lads were always paid off in the summer. Once he was told there was more money with the firm of Wyllies. "The Charlton boys told me I wouldn't stay twenty-four hours—I was there for forty-five years" Joe told me in his retirement which is spent only two or three streets away from the former mill depot in Dumfries.

After about five years as assistant—'second man' in the millman's parlance—he got the driver's job on the Burrell. Wyllies' mill team included a Ransomes, Sims and Jeffries unit and also Clayton tractors but Joe always had charge of the big Burrell which weighed something like twelve tons. Trailing a four-ton mill, a three-ton 15 cwt baler and a 30 cwt caravan, he ran one of the Kirkcudbrightshire circuits, usually starting at Auchenfad farm and the neighbouring Hall farm at Auchencairn. They had their corn sown in the first week of March and were usually first to need the threshers.

The drivers' duties on the road were to concentrate completely on the hand controls of the old 'steamers' while the second man did the steering, mostly at around 7 m.p.h. A two and a half-hour eighteen-mile pull from Dumfries to Castle Douglas could mean three halts for water and the working circuit often meant staying away from his Dumfries home for a week.

"I've seen me getting home at ten o'clock on a Saturday night and having to leave with the four o'clock bus on the Sunday afternoon to return to where we had left the mill so that we could get the steamer kindled up again for the Monday morning," said Joe. "We finished sometimes at Borgue, near Kirkcudbright at six o'clock on a Saturday, perhaps shifted the mill to a farm near Castle Douglas and then biked home after that."

"When you landed at a farm at night you always set the mill ready for starting the next morning. We had two double beds in the van. The driver slept on his own but the second and third men shared the same bunk. We had chaff beds in these early days and, of course, a coal stove.

"When I started as second man I was getting 38s. 8d and this was raised to £2. 12s when I became spare driver. When I was a constant driver it went up to £3. At the time I retired the basic rate was £18.05."

Always a believer in cleanliness and comfort, Joe insisted that when the millmen were staying in their van, clogs and boots had to be taken off when entering and a mat was put down at nights. These were often spent playing dominoes or reading western novels. Sometimes Joe would babysit for a farmer and his wife to allow them a night out.

Working days in the steam engine era usually started at 6 a.m. to get steam up for 7 a.m. launch to the threshing. Byre lamps were sometimes hung on the mill to provide enough light for the driving belts to be set. The Burrell engine which Joe drove displayed acetylene lamps. He recalls an especially bright one on the front axle which had large mirror reflectors and "was good as any electric lamp".

Everybody knew the sight of the Coulthart mill on the road because of his lights. They remembered others on the byways too. Though they seldom met in with other mills on their journeys there was the occasional meeting with the likes of Willie Burns of Charltons and David McMinn of Derbys a firm in Castle Douglas which also had the travelling threshers. Such meetings led to "a right old chin wag," said Joe. "We sometimes met John McIntosh of Carsewells—a Dalbeattie firm—and we did not know whether it was a threshing mill or Blackpool illuminations because there were so many lights."

Joe's Burrell had solid rubber tyres and it seems that while some mills with metal wheels had difficulties in beating winter road conditions, Joe always got to his destination. Though there was one occasion on Auchencairn when the Burrell "lost her feet" on the frosty conditions and swept back down the shore road out of control. Home Guard members put horse dung and ashes on the road to allow a grip for re-starting.

"The slippy roads sometimes meant many hours for shifts between farms and I remember in a snowstorm once I could hardly see the funnel," said Joe. He added: "But we always got to our destination".

He considers the old Burrell "the most reliable thing on the highway." She went through eight hundredweights of coal plus big gallonages of water on a threshing day. The coal was usually provided by the farmers.

For every farm Joe had probably a tale—about the farmers, the helpers, the meals or the loanings and stackyards. He can recall up to twenty-two people "neighbouring" at a threshing under the traditional scheme where a farmer would enlist all his neighbours or their staff for such jobs as threshings or sheep shearing.

Most threshing visits meant only one day at a particular farm. Earlier in the season some farms which had big dairies needed two days. Joe reckons good progress was being made if they got through four stacks in the forenoon and four in the afternoon.

"Folks thought it was a cushy job," he recalls. "It was far from it. It was stoorie and it was hard work. I have seen us starting at six in the morning and finishing up at midnight with the rest of the day our own!"

Joe's threshing career which had begun as third man one day at Glengower farm near Holywood in Dumfriesshire — the shift the next day was to Ellisland, once farmed by Robert Burns — ended at Cowdens, near Lockerbie with the last work for his mill coming in the days when the self-propelled combine harvesters were coming into vogue.

By that time Joe had progressed from steam to petrol and diesel tractors. He drove an Oliver 80, an International, a McCormick W9, and latterly a David Brown 50D (OSM 472) with which he pulled his tackle for about fourteen years. "I once went from Dumfries to Twynholm with a mill, a baler and a 'van and didn't need to change a gear," says Joe eulogising about the David Brown. And he once brought the whole line-up back from Borgue to Dumfries in 1½ hours — a time nearly equalled by cars now in the A75's thick Irish-orientated traffic.

"I wasn't sorry to leave the steam but when I started on the tractor I used to keep running out of paraffin and things like that. I had had no experience of tractor driving beforehand and was just shoved into the job."

But they were more comfortable days for, as he says, the old steam engine was alright "as long as the rain was coming straight down. But if it was blowing from the sides into the cabin it was like standing up a tree on a wet night." What helped to keep him warm in these climes was Hutchison's famed Dumfries-made clogs and these he constantly refilled with straw wisps for added warmth.

Joe finished his days with a Garvie mill behind his David Brown and the threshing operation was costing the farmer about £3 an hour compared to 7s. 6d. when he started in the 1920s. Throughout his mill days Joe followed the motto of his fisherman father: "A place for everything and everything in its place." His neatness meant he could find any tool in the darkness of the van without the need of a light.

There were days of humour and jests too. There is the classic yarn told by jovial Joe of the day he was creeping with his heavy and lengthy train — tractor, thresher, baler and mobile bothy — up the lonesome Water of Ken hidden deep in the sheep rills between Carsphairn and Moniaive in the Galloway-Dumfriesshire borderland to thresh the oats at Holm of Dalquhairn, a farm kindly cradled under the high hill ground and near the end of the valley road.

"What's ower the back o' that hill Joe? queried the young lad who was a mill assistant, as Joe himself had been many years before. The lad was new to this silent pastoral world. "Ower there?" says Joe pointing to the Lorg hill which seals the top of the glen. "Ower there at the back o' yon hill son? That's where ye get the ferry fur the Orkneys lad." "Is it," said the boy credulously. "A' didnae ken it wis that near." Under his bonnet Joe straightfacedly drove on to the Holm with one youngster a little wiser about the layout of the land.

Happily Joe got another chance to drive a mill outfit. My article on his life in *The Scottish Farmer* was read by Ralph Allardyce of West Linton who, over the years had acquired as a hobby a complete mill unit which he takes round shows such as local agricultural events and vintage and veteran gatherings. Ralph invited Joe, in his retirement, to travel to Edinburgh to drive the 14½ ton 80-foot long train past the grandstand and ringside thronged with thousands of spectators at the 1978 Royal Highland Show.

At the head of their team was a 1947 Field Marshall tractor which had been found lying abandoned on its side in a field. The mill was one of the last built in 1951 by Ransomes Sims and Jeffries with a Ruston Hornsby straw trusser. There was a Fisher Humphries wire baler and a mill van, then thought to be about seventy-eight years old. All had been carefully restored by Ralph and friends and were as good as new.

Joe got a lift to the Highland Show, donned neckerchief, put his bonnet to racing angle, waved to the crowd and "thoroughly enjoyed" getting together with the machinery of the past as he sat behind the steering column of the Field Marshall and puttered past a crammed grandstand.

The roads in Dumfriesshire and the Stewartry of Kirkcudbright throbbed with travelling mills belonging to many other firms—Robinsons, Browns, Johnstones, Kingans, South West Farmers and Clanachans to name only a small number.

I was told more of the life of the mill-tenders by the late Robert Warbeck who shared his memories with me in 1969 in his Lochmaben home. He too had been on Ruston Proctors with their full heads of steam.

"We could make about sixteen miles an hour. The old engine itself weighed eleven tons, then there was the mill weighing five tons and the 30 cwt van behind that. Mind you, the tractor when it came, was handier and quicker to move from place to place. But for workmanship, steam was the thing," said Robert.

In partnership with George Pattie, his father had three mills during the mid-1930's. Machines fit to grace any stackyard. It was the best of tackle and costing around £600 new per turnout to buy. The van used for night stays was made locally.

With a full winter of threshing round the roads of Moffat, Johnstone, Ecclefechan, Boreland and Dalton in Dumfriesshire, the chocolate-coloured mills of Warbeck and Pattie steamed to a fair mileage. Robert had a few years as second man before taking over as driver. But even as second man he had to ride in the traction unit's cabin with perhaps a sheet thrown round on a cold or wild day to halt some of the weather.

A tender on the engine carried about four or five hundredweights of coal.

Robert and his mate would sleep in the van from the Sunday night to the next Friday night if the shifts between farms were any distance. He could recall leaving the mill at Moffat on a Saturday and having to rise at 4.30 a.m. on the Monday to cycle there from his home at Lochmaben, arriving after 2½ hours of pedalling. And after that it took an hour and a half to get steam up.

On his changeover from second man to driver he said: "The 'steamers' were alright to drive. When I first started I thought I would never manage but after getting into the way, I was as good as my father at it."

Roads were not so busy then and a steam unit pulling the mill and the van by carbine lamps was not an unusual sight at nights as he steamed on to get the tackle to a new site ready for the morning.

"We could make and consolidate many a farm road with the turnout," Robert recalled. "When the farmers knew we were coming—I used to send out postcards saying when I would be there—they put down stones so that we would flatten them in to repair their roads. Not only in the loanings but also in the stackyards.

His 1908 Ruston Proctor had three gears. A lot of brasswork had to be continually polished. In the summer he serviced the whole outfit so that it was mechanically sound for the next winter of work.

Like other millmen he had to take his share of either looking after the tackle or feeding in the cut sheaves when the hum of the thresher started. 'Mind the knives' was a common shout when a 'lowser'—the person who cut the strings on the sheaves before dropping the oats into the threshing drum—dropped a knife. Similarly with stones, as the biggest danger came if they were catapulted back up from the mill's inside reels. "So if anything went in we shut the trap door on top," said Robert.

On wet days the millmen often had to stay inside their van if they were a fair distance from home. "It was warmer than a house," Robert remembered.

The canniness of the millman meant he did not, or tried not to, haul his equipment far in winter's worst weather. And in the summer there were further problems with the old steamer wheels. When tar melted on a hot day the millmen could only move on the road at nights for fear of lifting the tar with the metal wheels.

The rewards for this life of oat stoor, gritty chaff and coal grime? "There was a good lot of money in the steam days at the threshings but not when the tractors came, for there was a lot more wear and tear" according to Robert Warbeck.

His first wage would be about fifty shillings as a second man and it went up to five pounds when he became a driver.

Not all the threshing was done in stackyards. A lot was carried out in fields where the farmers had built the stacks in a handy corner adjacent to gates. Robert said "You had to watch you did not sink. We would 'heel' the ground with our boots to see if it would carry. Sometimes about a dozen spade-lugs would be put on each of the traction engine unit's wheels to ensure it did not bog down."

Robert reckoned they could thresh seven or eight ricks in a day or two or three 'soo' ricks. These were lengthy stacks bigger than some of today's bungalows.

Robert's steam engine days ended just after the 1939-45 war when his firm moved into tractors and re-fitted the threshing units with rubber wheels. The old engines were sold at Carlisle, destined for scrap.

But he never had as much respect for the petrol and diesel tractors. He had a Fordson and a Lanz to begin with before the firm was taken over by Scottish Agricultural Industries (SAI) for whom he worked for another ten years until the arrival of the combine harvester.

Once a millman, then, always a millman. "It was a right dirty job sometimes but I liked the mill." said Robert with relish. "If you saw two millmen talking on a Saturday night you would know what they were talking about—mills."

But where nowadays will you see two millmen?

LAND OF THE MURRAYS

As hill sheep are hefted—they stay on their own demarcated ground—so too are a big number of shepherding families. It is not a geographical phenomenon, it just appears to be a natural inclination. Such men are able to recall the tales and feats of their forebears.

There are in our land's straths and glens and hills handed-down families of upland folk—men who follow in the footsteps of their fathers, their grandfathers and even ancestors far beyond that.

Of such legend are the Murrays, a much-respected line awash in hill lore and character. One goes back again and again to the company of John Murray to listen to the homely philosophy of a much-admired shepherd for such wisdom is worthy of passing on. There may be little time for it come another generation.

There are still duties for John including helping out at lambings. It is a long while since his first one when at twelve years of age in 1916 he got off school to help his legendary father Ben Murray lamb Blackfaces in raw Eskdalemuir, a glen once green and now an ocean of Sitka Spruce.

Those of us who saw in 1971 on a memorable sun-filled day John, far from his homeland hills, collect a waggonload of silver as the new International Sheep Dog Trials supreme champion in Cardiff, agreed he had been well rewarded for his forty-odd years of trying for the blue riband. Not just for the winning drove on Welsh mountain sheep that afternoon with the gleg mottle-faced collie Glen, but also for a lifetime's devotion and care to hill sheep which still continues today when he is within two decades of his century.

It all stems from the craft and skill gained in his everyday tending of sheep on the high places since he first, as a full-time shepherd, lifted a crook and called his dog to heel on the Fardenmulloch hirsels of Craigdarroch farm above the Nith. That was back in 1923 and now, in retirement near Sanquhar in Dumfriesshire, he lives practically within sight of his first sheep work.

Though there were other respected sheepmen to run their dogs that 1971 afternoon at Cardiff, John knew when he herded off his sheep at the loudly-applauded end of his drove, that he had won. We Scots knew it too. Elated? "Not one wee bit, it was jeest like coming off the hill," John told me.

The analysts would have some fancy way of interpreting that quotation. But what it boils down to is this—it was a job of work for a man of the hills whose foremost thoughts are for the care of his sheep. It was an example of a collie, kept, broken and trained primarily for its everyday duties on the hills giving a classic example of its role in different circumstances—a role of patience, study, natural ability, initiative, obedience, alertness and response to command.

It is something which does not come overnight. In John Murray's case it came through at least two generations. And nowadays, unfortunately, there are those who breeze to a football-pitch-sized sheepdog trials field with dogs jerking here and there to every command—and this can consist sometimes of a ten minute hail of wheeps and shouts—but which have lost all natural ability and initiative.

These will never, one hopes attain the status of Glen nor the dogs whose blood he carries, dogs which use their own heads when far out on the hills. The mechanised movements are not for our glens and high hefts. There is still the place for traditions of old for man and his four-legged companion. Men who speak the tongue like John Murray.

As he puts it: "The 'herd has an awful lot to study. You have to have great patience with sheep and study them all along the line. You just do not go to the hill with boots, dog and stick. That does not make you a shepherd. You must never be in a hurry. Running is no use. Take time to study."

The mood is smittling. Even to the stock John attended for, though long retired, he occasionally helps out at busy times. One laggardly old newly-lambed ewe which we came across by a burnside of the Bogg farm hirsels when I went round the hill with John at lambing time in the early 70's and destined to be driven for the night's shelter in a dyked park got this homely advice: "Come on aul' yin, jeest toddle alang. Y're daein' fine. Ye'll be as yauld as a hare efter a nicht ben the park."

As we strode the hill pads taking everything—ewes, lambs and hoggs—before us to the higher ground for the night, the stock were under the able joint guardianship of the speckle-fronted Glen and the champion's black-coated son Hemp, a youngster at his first lambing and an admirable collie to watch, like his sire, when sent far over burns and bracken to turn back some blue-keeled hoggs which had strayed from their hefts. And as gentle as need be when following ewes and their lambs.

"You have to be careful how you hunt the sheep at all times," said John. "There are the drains for instance. You can make an awful mess if you just send the dog away any old way to gather sheep. You need a nice canny dog at lambing time. One that will keep back and give the ewes room. But again there is the time you need a firm one as well when you want to catch a ewe."

Glen was bred at the Bogg farm when John herded there full-time and I remember seeing him as a ten-month pup. He had started running at four months old and he turned into a natural follower. Championship blood runs in the family. Glen's sire was the tall cock-luggit Wiston Cap

47

which won the supreme trials title in Cardiff in 1965 and which played a prominent part in the breeding pattern of the Border collies for many years.

Cap's owner John Richardson and John Murray shared many cheery times at trials. There is a yarn told of them when—supposedly though it may be true—they went to Majorca for a holiday and were lazing in the sun watching bikini-clad young maidens wobble past.

"What day is it Jock," asks John Murray of his fellow herd.

"What day John? It's New Cumnock Sheepdog Trials day," replies John Richardson.

"So it is, so it is," says John Murray. "Man but they're gettin' a right guid day for it."

A way with words led John Murray to exporting one of his collies when in an article in *The Scottish Farmer* in 1968 I quoted him as saying one of his young collies Bob was a 'thunderin' guid dog.' It so captivated the late Ben Wilson, one of the country's most respected sheep men, that he bought it unseen and sold it to the U.S.

The Glen dog, which was to become one of the most watchable trials collies I have ever seen as he plied so willingly to John Murray's quiet distinctive whistle commands, was out of his own black, blue, mottled and white bitch Katy. Katy was by Sharp's Lad out of J. T. M. Thomson's Guess with some noted Ayrshire and Wigtownshire blood including Bunt Hyslop's Lad, John Thomson's Flo and Maid, Jim Millar's Drift and David Young's Meg.

When I first saw Glen as a pup and John told me he had started shaping for his work at four months old, he added: "They can be learning a lot at three or four months. Even obedience in going into their kennels is teaching them something. There are a lot of things you can learn them before going near sheep. And when ready they'll be as yauld as a hare."

It is a quotation with the tang of the blow-bent grass and the drawmoss and the lilting land John and his kind have always strode. He used it once when he told me about his grandfather, Thomas Murray, the much respected shepherd-poet, a tall, bearded 'herd who came from Eskdalemuir into the quiet Water of Ken in Galloway's hill fastness well over a century ago and whose writings are still read in glen cottages. This was perhaps where the Murray legend began. Certainly a lot of it was fashioned by Thomas Murray, the chronicler of the silent heights who herded long in the Ken and its neighbouring water, the Deugh, beyond Carsphairn where sheep no longer graze.

I will return to write of Thomas Murray but must again pass on some of the wisdom of John Murray given to me in a fireside crack at his cheery Sanquhar home not long after winning the Cardiff International Trials of 1971. I still consider it to be the best interview I ever achieved—not for any literary merit for it merely passed on the sound and sincere thoughts of a much-loved man. No poet could pen the thoughts of a true hill man when describing the year's toughest spell—lambing time—better than John in these remarks.

"You get fed up in lambing times whiles when you land in bothers. But it works past. And come the beginning of June things are beginning to improve and you forget the troubles. Then in the mornings when you are out and see the lambs dancing and playing away when they come down the hill, you think it is grand.

"You can be standing at the top of the hill yourself. The birds start whistling and the grouse are laughing and cackling. You see every ewe whacking down the pad with a lamb behind her and you think it is an awful nice sight in the morning.

"Even the old hares might stop, sit up and rub their forelegs together as much as if to say: 'Good morning, it's nice to be alive.' You forget about the struggle you have had and you feel you have won the battle. I had the same feeling as I came off the field at Cardiff."

Those of us who had watched John Murray's progress with Glen had the notion it would end that way. There was one who thought once John might not make a success of things—his father Ben Murray—a name oft mentioned and passed on by those thirled to the weave of dogs and sheep. A master at handling and breeding dogs and, of course, tending sheep.

"I learned everything off my father as far as sheep and dogs were concerned," John told me. "Of course you gain a lot of experience by yourself once you are into it. But at one time he thought I would not make a success of it because I was too quick-tempered and too strict. He thought I was too regimental. He did not tell me that, but I know he told other folk. I have learned since you have not to be so quick. You must take time and have patience. But I kept in mind all the things he told me and he was right."

Later John's thoughts were sharpened, polished and weathered through a career which began in the days when his tasks included droving to Lanark market and on through hirsel-tending duties of hill flocks in the Lammermuirs, Muirkirk, Ayrshire and Dumfriesshire. And also a career of bringing out Blackface rams including Lanark's dearest one in October 1951, a £1,400 sale from Nether Whithaugh to Whitehope, home then of the greatest sheepdog man of them all, the late J. M. Wilson whose collies' blood featured so strongly in the trials dogs of John Murray.

"Aye, father talked a lot," said John. "I whiles did not go along with it, but always kept in mind what he said. He sat and cracked to us all night about training dogs. You were listening all the time and taking it all in. I have remembered a lot of things he told us and they were right."

There would be a crack too on these nights of Ben's own great successes with collies. But work came first. And here, more of Ben's advice was followed by the young John and moulded into the half-century and more of sheep work which followed.

"You have to have great patience with sheep. You have to study them all along the line. You have to watch for the odd one failing and get her in for feeding or treatment before she is too far down in her health. It is no use waiting until she needs a spade. You should get to know the good milking strains. And if you do not dauner among them and study them you do not get to learn these things.

"You get to know nearly them all. As you journey on you can say, 'there's old brockit-face or grey nose' and so on. You might have nicknames for most of them. I never did boast about knowing them all, but I knew all those I needed to know.

"Two dogs are enough on the hill. They are a big help, one on each side of the sheep. It's gey sair on one dog at lambing time if you get some wild sheep which will not stick together. But two were always enough with me. You could maybe take a young one out in the morning to teach for the gatherings.

"Always remember to keep sheep on the move. It keeps them fit. They get as lazy as tramps if they are not shifted about. Going to the hill to look them twice a day is enough, although at lambing time you should be wandering among them most of the time.

"Always be off your hill by five o'clock. You should not be among them after that. They are better left alone. Leave them to graze in peace and do not bring them down the hill too early in the morning. If you are away at 7 o'clock that is early enough. A lot of the old mens' notions were all wrong. Getting away early at lambing time was a piece of nonsense. You had no need. A lot of the old boys created unnecessary work and it wasn't for any good,"

Like every hill 'herd John had his share of winter's storms. "I've seen some flaming storms. The worst I knew was in 1917 at the head of Eskdalemuir when my father was at Nether Cassock. It snowed every night and was fair through the day. Sheep were buried all over the place—I remember looking for them. The next worst would be in 1933. It started snowing on a Saturday night and did not stop until the Monday morning. A lot of sheep were lost that time."

To be fair, John says there are times when an early start in the morning is needed—at gatherings for the clipping. "If it is good weather get away before the sun is up and have the sheep in before the sun rises. They are far easier to gather in the early morning."

There were other times too in those droving days when a 4 a.m. start was necessary. John could recall three-day droves from Craigdarroch in the Nith Valley to Lanark sales, staying the nights at the homesteads of fellow shepherds on the way.

And on one occasion sheep were walked up Crawick Water then entrained for a trip to Symington where the sale was being held, foot-and-mouth disease restrictions having stopped its progress at Lanark. "Our ewes made 28s. that day. I always remember that night. I stayed in a cottage and was awake all night killing fleas that were crawling all over me."

The Murray legend, as I mentioned earlier, had begun with his grandfather Thomas, a shepherd-poet whose book I value greatly. A shepherd for over sixty years and one, who, like many who tend the green ground are close to their Maker. Thomas Murray sifted his thoughts during his tramps among the braes and penned them at the ingle at night. Sometimes they were long nights and he would break off to whittle away fashioning a new crook.

In 1970 I set out to gather material on Thomas Murray and met many of his descendants. It is sadly ironic that, looking through the history of this storyteller I found he was born at Castle O'er, Eskdalemuir, now part of one of Scotland's largest forests, and penned most of his words near part of the high-lying Carsphairn region of Galloway which will also become one of the biggest of tree complexes. I return throughout this book to the encroachment of forestry but anyone who tries to track down the legends of hill people in South Scotland cannot avoid this.

The folk-poet himself viewed, worriedly, changes even back then around the 1880's when he and a companion set off from the hills of Galloway on a ramble over to Tweed which resulted in one of his best poems:

> And sae we saw 'twas ae instance
> O' mony hames passed frae existence
> The fouk gane into towns or clachans
> There for their risin' offspring's crappin's
> May hae a parritch pat tae lick
> But what instead o' hawkie's milk
> Sae suited stalwart frames to rear up
> A slake o' treacle or o' syrup
> And wi' regret we came to feel
> This canna be for Scotland's weal
> As country hames pass oot o' fashion
> Rustics maun dwindle in proportion.

This poem is one of many in a book of Tom Murray's rhymes and songs published in the late 1890's. His companion that day was Jim Robertson, a shepherd from Glennoch, deeper into the Carsphairn hills and now uninhabited. I met Jim Robertson's sons Ned and Bob in Sorn. Ned, who had been a shepherd all his days, including a spell at the head of Loch Doon, recalled one day during his Wigtownshire tendings "seeing a body coming from the hill near Dalhabbloch, New Luce. I couldn't understand what it was and dallied my step. At first I thought it was a woman, but after it came closer I saw it was Tom Murray in a plaid."

John Murray told me of his grandfather: "He never had a coat and leggings in his life. It was always the plaid he wore. I remember he always carried ginger snaps to eat on the hills and he often handed some to us youngsters."

Thomas Murray's former cottage home at Moorbrock, Carsphairn housed a shepherd's collies when I was last there. But at one time it would be a happy abode from where the folk-poet penned many words of wisdom on everyday happenings—and also messages to the shopkeepers when he required any goods sent to him at the remote spot. Like the time he posted off a note to Thomas Little, a travelling grocer who hied deep into the upland Galloway tracts and called at the cottage where Thomas Murray then stayed at the Holm of Dalquhairn. Or the Holm of Ken as it was known to some.

> At Holm o' Ken, o' Januar' drear
> Nicht, twenty-third in the young year
> O' eighteen hundred and eighty
> Dear Tammas, I sit down to write ye
> When first ye up this valley drive
> I wish ye'd bring frae Moniaive
> Or onywhere for you maist handy
> New clogs, a pair, for oor wee Sandy
> His only pair are turned ower little
> Or's feet for them are turned ower meikle
> Whatever way you like to state it
> But mark my wish, and no' forget it
> I'm wae to hear and see the urchin
> Wi' childblains whimperin' and hirplin'
> Enclosed herewith a tape ye'll get—
> That's the exact length o' his fit
> Sae trustin' ye'll get a' in time
> And pay attention to my rhyme
> I shall remain until ye hurry
> Your humble debtor, Tammas Murray.

Robert Grierson, grandson of Tom Murray and living at the time near Keir village in Dumfriesshire, told me: "Grandfather was an awful man to write when he came in. At night he would sit for hours. And no doubt he was putting the verses together on the hills. He had a lot of books and was always reading," a remark borne out by John Murray who added: "It would not matter what you asked him about the Bible, he would be able to answer you."

Much of his writings came from the oddities and adventures of life. This is how he instructed a Newton Stewart auctioneer to sell his pig:

> "Dear sir, as grey gloamin' is gatherin' roun'
> And sternies peep through the dark clouds that are big
> While here I sit musing, pray listen my croon
> And I'll gie ye instructions concerning my pig.
> He's ane o' a litter I ken-na frae whaur

52

But that doesna matter a groat or a fig
  I bought, paid and marked him
  Eelstabbed i' the na'r
    Sae that if I lost I could swear to my pig
I hadna a mind for to sell him sae sun
  But if he's no wally, he's plump fat and trig
And meal being dear, and the pratties near dune
    There's naething for me but dispose o' my pig.
I ettled to come wi' the creature mysel'
  But duty does call me elsewhere for to jig
That makes nae ae plack for yer story ye'll tell
  And he that nods langest maun jist get the pig.
But after a' jokin' keep mind I am poor
  And sae wi' yer bidders persistently prig
Declare he's a neat ane and wechty ye're sure
  And I trow ye will get the worth o' my pig
Meanwhile, sire, gude speed, ye will ken what I mean
  And some day, if spared, we will baith hae a swig
When first at the town I'm maist sure to keep min'
  To gie ye a ca' for the price o' my pig."

Thomas Murray had great sympathy with nature. It came out in
verses written when he found a laverock killed after flying against
telegraph wires:

      So justly do I tune my lay
    In memory, sweetest bird, of thee
      For oft, when Spring was fresh and gay
    Thy sang has been delight to me

      And while I rove o' you bereft
    This ae sweet hope shall keep me fain
      That ye hae routh o' offspring left
    Weel tutored in their mither strain

      Accept, sweet charmers o' the heath
    This tribute frae my friendly lyre
      And henceforth try to skim beneath
    Or mount abune that fatal wire.

Among the grey reek swirling into nothingness from the proud haggis
in January there are many who pay tributes running into thousands of
words to the Bard. Many emerge from the vacuum to speak fluently of
Rabbie. They have done it for generations and will continue to do so.
Thomas Murray, sadly a less-remembered poet, was among the countless
moved by Burns' work. He paid his own tribute:

53

O' a' the favoured tunefu' birds
Oor Robin sings the best
His strains directly touch the chords
And kirnel o' the breast

Whate'er his theme, on war's alarms
Or characters may be
On friendship, love, or Nature's charm
Nae paint sae true as he.

Thomas Murray had his own style too. His are the genuine words of a concerned poet re-telling the essence of life in the outbye world not only of Galloway but of Scotland's uplands. They will form a valuable part of history when many of the places he writes of will no longer be on the map.

The schools in that area are already gone. More will follow. And I know who will be to blame. Yet just over 100 years ago Thomas Murray was fighting to bring them to his own glen. He has talked about the martyrs of the old days and the shepherds and he added:

True patriots, they respect the Queen
And ilka law ootmeted fare
But tyranny or actions mean
Their study natures ill can bear;
Yet what they've fought for lang and sair
Schule privilege as meant for a'
The Schule Board still in that to share
Denies their pairt o' Gallowa'
A teacher fit to gie them lore
A schule built ticht, and dry abune
Wi' sittin's for a lucky score
Wad meet oor cares and change oor tune
Wad grace oor bonnie upland vale
And honour its promoters a'
And thro' the future scarce could fail
To profit fair, auld Gallowa'

There are those of us, weaned on the words of James Hogg and the lesser hill folklorists who see in their words, expression and feeling comparable and perhaps with more clarity and satisfaction than those of Burns in portraying the outlying hill world. Yet Hogg and the likes of John Dickson, 'Blue Bell' and Thomas Murray gain little recognition or remembrance these days.

Thomas Murray was a far-seeing poet. Here is the whole of his poem "Sawners and Tammas, or, the Kirk or the Hill?" This is Tom Murray at his best. His words are well worth studying.

Oot last Sunday morning set Sawners
When keen blew the wind frae high west;
   He met by the way neebour Tammas,
And thus they each other addrest;

"What fettle the day?" began Sawners,
"Are a' weel aboot yer fire-en?"
   "We're a' weel, I thank ye," quo Tammas
"And I houp ye a' bravely do fen."

"We're a' in a way," replied Sawners.
"Oor several tasks to fulfil,
   "Are ye oot for the kirk?" "Na," quo Tammas,
"I'm jist on my way to the hill."

"A-weel, if ye're that way decided,
   I'll jist hae to wag on my lane;
But the hill there wad naething betide it,"
   Quo Sawnie wi' serious mein.

Quo Tammas, "This wild, gurly weather
   Wid dad the sheep a' to the deil;
Aroun the ootskirts I maun daunner,
   And wile the puir things to a beil,"

"Noo, frien, if it had been a waddin,' "
   Wi' emphasis Sawnie did say,
"Wad fear o' this strayin' and daddin'
   Hae kept ye as it does the day?"

"We aye hae the chance o' a sermon,
At least once a week, and its clear
   The waddin's are far mair uncommon,
I rarely get ane in the year."

"Ye're never ill aff for an answer,
But try and keep reason in view;
   How oft does our reverend pastor
Pray ower yer unoccupied pew?"

"It's true I'm nae deep debater,
But settin' a' forms to the side,
   Say, can I no praise my Creator
Alane where the muirlan' streams glide?"

"That's better a vast, and we canna
Deny that it sae far is richt;
   The dwellings o' Jacob He'll shun-na
Yet Zion he eyes wi' delight."

"He sees when oor duties require us
Aback frae His House for to stay,
And to praise Him if love doth inspire us
He'll hear us, do that where we may.

"In days when oor sturdy forefathers
'Gainst darkness stood up for the licht,
Frae kirks and hames chased in a' weathers,
Your view in sic cases is richt.

"But noo your excuse is like nonsense,
The han's o' the despot are staid;
We can worship according to conscience
Nane daurin' to mak' us afraid.

"The kirk's word is 'welcome a' comers,'
The Master invites a' to share
His message sent through her to sinners,
And we, when we can, should be there.

"And wha the advantage refuses,
And suffers his conscience to streek.
And builds upon heartless excuses,
Is wrang, jist as sure as I speak."

Quo' Tammas, "Ye're awsome in knowledge,
Whaur gat ye sic language and wit?
Were ye trained in a club or a college?
Or whaur that sae straught ye can hit?"

"I never had knowledge to brag o', "
Quo Sawnie, touched near to the quick,
"But that's no the question we argue,
Say noo, are ye gaun to the kirk?"

"I'd hae to gar hame for a jacket,
The preachin' at twal' does begin
And ere I got there, the plain fac' o't
Is this, I wad be clean ahin.' "

"The Maister respects nae the jacket,
The heart that is humble alane,
He looks to, and ne'er will mistak' it
Beneath a coarse jacket or nane."

"I still think oor gracious Maister
Allows us attention to pay
To a' sorts o' stock o' the pasture,
And if rang to richt them the day."

"That's truth if ye'd ground for to back it,
But noo the occasion's sae sma'
    Nae lambin', nae coupin', nane maukit,
Nor fear o' them smoorin' wi' snaw."

Quo Tammas, "The cauld I think's plenty
To mak' ane slip roun' the high grun,'
    And turn in wide wanderers gently,
They'll snugger lie under the wun.' "

"Yet them we had risked for a waddin'
As verra weel micht ye indeed,
    But time's wearing on, are ye comin'?"
Tam answered by shakin' his heid.

"I wish ye gude-day, then" quo Sawners,
And forward he pressed wi' a will,
    "He's heavy this day," muttered Tammas,
And pensively slade to the hill.

Sae ended their lengthy discussion;
Tho' Tam never fairly gave way,
    His neebour's words left an impression
May bear fruit on some other day.

THE 'HERDS FAIRS

Shepherds' Suppers are still held in a few townships and villages in South Scotland and the Borders. They are almost the only reminder of past days when shepherds met annually to claim or report straying sheep. Like any foregathering of the hill fraternity they were big social affairs.

There are at least a couple of howffs I know where once a year the hill men hunt for stray sheep.

From herdings in South Ayrshire and Galloway they are continuing, at the likes of the Rowantree and New Cumnock Herds Fairs, a tradition which started on the raw heights of that sheep country a century ago.

On the high, desolate road winding over from Bargrennan to Barr and Straiton in South Ayrshire—once sound Blackface country but now damned and blanketed by trees—shepherds met near the Rowantree Toll in 1882 and founded the Rowantree Herds Fair.

Today, along with the big-drawing New Cumnock function, it is one of the few fairs left. Though the Rowantree one started at the gusty toll-gate and was also held at nearby Suie, it has, since 1885, been celebrated in Barr village, mostly in the Jolly Shepherds' Hotel, an aptly named establishment for the cheery herds banter of a wild winter's night. And there can be some in that airt.

At both Rowantree and New Cumnock, the legend of these first 'Herds' Fairs is carried on today. Sometime during the evening the chairman calls for any stray sheep to be reported. If shepherds' have any on their hefts they bring details of the markings and these are announced. Should there be no claimants the sheep are auctioned and if not claimed after an advertisement appears in the local newspapers, the proceeds go to local charities.

Throughout all these eventful years, herd's widows, retired shepherds and local school, kirk and hospitals have benefitted. At the 1967 Rowantree event seventy-five people attended the supper at the Fair, and later on 200 were at the dance. "We had another happy and memorable night," said Mr Duncan McKenzie of Bargany Mains, Dailly, who was secretary.

There was no stray sheep reported that time, and in all the years I have managed to get to the New Cumnock 'Herds Fair, held just before Christmas, there has also been silence when the chairman called "any strays to report?"

It was not always so, as a look at the minute book of both Fairs indicates. The minutes of the Rowantree event showed that it started on

58

22 December 1884 and the names of many at that meeting—Pringle, Stewart, Kirkland, McCutcheon, Galloway, Welsh, Burns, Wilson, Murdoch—are still to be found among herding families who attend the present-day Fairs.

Minutes of that 1884 meeting at which it was decided to have the Fair at Barr, though retaining the Rowantree title, show there were seven shillings in hand. First stray sheep are mentioned in 1886. A Blackface ewe found on Craig was bought by David McQuatter at £1 while a wedder (castrated male sheep) made 11s. 6d. to Hugh McHarg. In 1890 the proceeds provided twenty-nine poor people in the parish each with half a pound of tea. The total cost was £1. 9s.

Though the first world war halted the event, the money was sent each year to the Red Cross and when the event re-started in 1919 admission charges to the dance were 6d for ladies and 2s. 6d. for men. There were three stray sheep that time and retired shepherds and widows each got £1.

The Fair became even more popular after the second world war. The minutes of the November 1947 meeting ended with the sombre note—"All members of committee have the power to deal with any disturbance in the 'Jolly' (Jolly Shepherds Hotel) or in the hall."

The cover of the thick and historical book of minutes of Rowantree 'Herds Fair contains these words written on the endpaper:

> Let the wealthy and great
> They may roll in their state;
> I envy them not I declare it.
> I eat my own lamb,
> My chicken and ham;
> I shear my own fleece
> And I wear it.

The minute book of the New Cumnock Herds Fair gives the organisation its full title—'Journal Proceedings of the Store Masters of the Parish of New Cumnock, Instituted on 14 August 1787.' Unfortunately the minutes of the first three years cannot be found so the story began on 10 August 1790 at Old Miln farm where eleven strays were given up.

The sheepman's own language bringing in their ear marks and body marks are well spread throughout the minute book in describing the strays. That year from Craigman for instance, the minutes record the strays as being from Craigman farm "a wether sheep back hal'f and fore hal'f the far," from Dalgig, "three lambs, cutted in the near—spained;" from Garrive, "a ewe hogg, eel stabbed in the near and back nipped in the far, burns but not distinguishable;" and from Craigdarroch "an old yell ewe, back halfed in the near, back halfed and cutted the far, a burn from near week to near eye."

Money came into the New Cumnock Herds' Fair in other ways as well as the auction of strays. At that 1790 meeting two men "failed to attend here this day" and the meeting fined them 2s. 6d. each.

Delegates were sent to other Fairs being held at that time including Sanquhar and Kirkconnel to claim such sheep "as might be given up belonging to any members of the New Cumnock Society." A delegate, around 1808, got 5s for attending both the Sanquhar Fair—nowadays diminished to a very popular carpet bowling tournament—and Kirkconnel Winter Fair.

Off Meiklehill farm that year came "a Mug ewe holed in both lugs with a whole lugged lamb," also "an old ewe eil stobbed the near and topped the far and ritted in both the stumps and an 'I' burn between the eyes to the top of the nose, but she being reported not to live was given to Mary Douglas."

The year 1854 must have been memorable. On the December day of the annual meeting "owing to a severe storm and one of the greatest floods ever known in the parish," the meeting was adjourned. I can recall one Fair in the 1960's too where folks from nearby Afton Water were unable to return home from the function because of a snowstorm which raged during the proceedings.

In 1875 for the first time there were no stray sheep to report and the situation was to crop up more often with the simple words "no business was done" being minuted.

It was in 1897 that the couthy hill poet Thomas Murray wrote about the Fair. Did he bring a fresh vigour and enthusiasm? It is possible. He wrote of the unceremonious event without need of a programme and singers being called to their feet. So it is even today with no need of accompaniment for a fine body of country folk who can sing and crack. Anybody is liable to be roped in to entertain the 300-odd who now attend it.

The event in fact began gradually to turn into a social occasion and for the first time ladies come into the picture in 1921. Three years later the minutes admitted: "These meetings are now taking a different form from what they did 100 years ago and this annual event is now what may be termed the shepherds gala." Items like music, advertising and floor polish crept into the expenditure side. After 1933 I can see no further mention of any stray sheep. In that year two sheep were given up as straying on Lochbrowan. They were claimed by Mr John Young, Polquhirter. So they may now remain a part of history.

The shepherds language, however, will always include the strange lore of the lug and keel marks of sheep. And one man whom I met who had a lot to do with this aspect was Harry Wales who had taken two years to gather together the markings of 564 flocks when I met him in 1970. Mind you, he had turned seventy-three.

But the mammoth and painstaking task was taken with the same sure, purposeful strides that for many decades rolled over the exposed open fells beyond and above his homestead in North Westmorland, now part of Cumbria.

From his experiences of the previous twenty years he could easily tell who in these vast North England sheepruns had the pop on the near hook; the sword stroke the far side; the near ear under-bit or the far one stowed; a rud pop on the drafts or the rud down the far shoulder.

There were 2,000 alternatives he could give. All the markings of the flocks in five North English counties were included in the 1½ lb. "Shepherds Guide" which Harry helped to produce every ten years.

He was in charge of the markings from the 564 flocks in the East Fells Association of which he had been secretary for twenty years when I visited him. There was a great pride in his chore, carrying on the tradition from the first meeting over 150 years previously when it was decided to bring out the guide.

Since then the weighty 700-plus-page tome has become for some the 'Flockmasters' Bible' and solved countless problems in identifying and tracing stray sheep on the fells. Even its sub-title "A proper delineation of the wool, horn and ear marks" has a proud ring to it.

The guide explains the procedure for flockmasters and shepherds to gather stray sheep on the moors or commons and take them to exchange meetings of stray sheep. For Harry Wales at that time, the principal meeting in the east was held twice a year at Gullum Holme.

With help from thirty-nine committee men in his own area—one man was appointed to each township—Harry had to distribute forms to flockmasters to fill in for the next guide. The farmer had to set out a description of horn burns, ear marks wool marks and rud marks.

First part of the guide gives a list of horn burns and ear marks. If, for example, a stray with the letters SE burned on the far horn turned up the finder would immediately look through the alphabetical list to find these letters and then an ear mark to go with them. Among ear marks listed are square fork, or key bit; cropped and stump slit; cropped and punch holed, fore shear slipe; dove tail bit, club ace bit, diamond punch hole and under slit. All referred to the shape of the cut.

The Wales family's own marking at Lownthwaite, near Milburn village, Penrith, was a L horn burn on both horns; near ear split; far ear stowed (cropped) with cross lambs slit on the near ear. The tar mark is an L on the near loin and an H on the far loin. Rud mark is on the rump with drafts (old ewes going off the higher ground) rudded on the back of the head or shoulder.

On the open fells of the Pennines, sheep can stray many miles and Mr Wales told me he had spent many an hour searching the guide to find markings when a stray turned up. There are about 2,000 markings in the four associations and it is reckoned no two flocks have the same combination.

I discovered during my call on Harry that sheep are not the only stock to have had a guide to their markings. He told me there was once a book of geese marks in the area. "I have not seen geese on the fells for about forty years but I remember as a youth my neighbour had a flock," he said. The geese flock markings were made by punching holes at different positions in the webbed section of their feet.

Another unique hill club I came across is the Upper Teviotdale Cow Club which is in existence to guard shepherds financially against the death of their own cows. Formed nearly seventy years ago it still has a very important function throughout many Border glens and waters for shepherds, cottagers or smallholders who have only one cow or perhaps the 'holders who might have ten.

Frank Charlton, manager at Waterhead of Dryfe, between Lockerbie and Eskdalemuir where he tended a carry of 1,100 Blackface hoggs and ewes and 145 cattle on 2,400 acres was secretary in the late 1970's. At that time there were 125 cows from the likes of Teviothead, Slitrig, Borthwickwater, Ewes, Westerkirk, Eskdalemuir, Ettrick, Yarrow, Dryfe, Waterbeck and Liddesdale valued in the club lists. This is a big extension on the original area, for, during the years other cow clubs have come and gone, several having been amalgamated into the Upper Teviotdale body.

The club began when the insurance premiums for the shepherd's cow were five shillings with the owner getting £15 if the cow died. In the late 1970's the fee had risen to £2.50 with £100 compensation but proposals at the time undoubtedly would lead to higher rates in that inflationary period.

The club's business, at that time, came in for discussion at four committee meetings a year and still follows the guidelines laid down when folk first sat down at Newmill School near Hawick in April 1918. The original meeting, according to the minutes, followed "a strong feeling throughout the Teviothead and Borthwick districts being given expression to in favour of starting a Cow Insurance Club for the insuring of cows belonging to cottagers, ploughmen, shepherds and smallholders."

At the first annual general meeting in 1919, eighty-nine cows had been entered on the roll and whist drives were started to boost funds. First claims were for two cows which died in 1920. Total cost was £30 plus veterinary fees of £3. 14s.

The 25th annual general meeting was celebrated with 185 cows on the list. Some years saw as many as seven claims on dead cows. These, of course, were mostly kept to provide milk for the shepherd's family and to help raise a couple of calves each year.

Like Herds Fairs, one of the most enjoyable functions of the Cow Club, is the social side with an annual dance. Discomania and whatever the fashion of its successor, cannot re-shape tradition and those who hand it down.

CROOKS GALORE

In the quiet of a winter night a pastoral craft which goes back to Biblical days is still very much alive in Scotland and in other hill areas of Britain. Many thousands of horn or wooden headed shepherds' crooks are carefully shaped and polished. The working crook is not an ornament. It has an important function in the sheep tender's everyday tasks.

Man and his dog are only two thirds of the pastoral yarn.

Our outbye world has another essential, a pivot without which our job could not be done. They have to be capable of holding a Blackface or a Cheviot going full flight down a hillside or bolting from the sheep yards. They must have balance too for the long trudges when their support, strength and company are needed by the hill folk.

Great cronies are shepherds crooks. No man is kitted out for the hill without one. Stopping a Blackie or a Cheviot is only a minor part of their work. There is no more amiable listener to the sound philosophies of the lone worker; no steadier vehicle to guide one back from the necessary business which delays us so often after a dog trial. There is their never-ending role on the hill, in the pens, at the market, shows and in the sale ring.

I have yet to see a man happy with one of these mass-produced aluminium objects. Or rather, a happy man with one. When one goes to the hill for twenty miles of rough country on sheep rakes amid heather and rock and scree, a man needs a stick which is well balanced, cheery and helpful.

The growing number of crookmaking classes in Scotland in the winter time—'schools for crooks' we call them—is a recognition of the need and the desire to keep the ancient craft of stickmaking alive. And it fairly is living. Dammit, a soul can hardly find a good horn or a decent hazel shank these days, so great is the demand. In fact some of us have sometimes to use a little stealth, and means which are perhaps round the back of legality, to get our raw material. But that is another tale altogether.

It is an individual craft. The old men have their own handed-down ways and it will always be so. My journeys among stick-men soon led me to the obvious fact—it is the same in sheepdog training and show and sale preparation of stock—that the maestros will only tell you half of their methods.

Some folk know a Goya or a Rembrandt. Some of us with a different slant on life can easily identify a Campbell, a MacDiarmid, a Brown, a Tulip, a MacKenzie, a Little or a Ri'path. Noted stickmen all of them with prizes galore to testify to their skills and with fifty per cent of their knowledge sealed off in their own minds.

We would-be Campbells, MacDiarmids, Tulips, Littles, Ri'paths and MacKenzie's plod away learning with our paraffin lamps, elbow grease, files and rasps, elbow grease, spittle, elbow grease, sharp-pointed and wife-annoying whittling knives, elbow grease and many, many disappointments.

Our basics are sound rams horns and good shanks, especially hazel and ash. There is always a saw hidden in a stickmaker's car boot, for the best time to cut a stick is just before somebody else sees it. Sometimes we rely, ahem, on the noted generosity of a famed Lordship—or, if you will have it another way, his absence—in allowing us to pursue our winter vocation by ungrudgingly 'gifting' us the occasional hazel shank from his healthily endowed little copse whose location I am not revealing. It is just one of the ironies of country life that when his pheasants and other game are carefully watched and guarded for fear of festive bird-snatchers, the stealthy stick-nicker goes to work.

(Some day, your worship, when the shanks are straight and the horns are sound, you will find there has been planked in the darkness of the night beside your front door, a crook of perfect curve and contour for your company, comfort and generosity. Thank you, thank you.)

Apart from a regular watch on marked hazel shanks in his Lordship's woods I was lucky in my travels among sheep tenders at obtaining well dried sticks from shepherds' byres and the likes. A soul just asked for them. But with horns the problem is worse. Our Blackface breeders nowadays in their search to gain the multi-thousand pound bid for their rams, tutor the young tups' horns with heat to fancify their shape. Some have adapted these gas camping burners or blowtorch-type efforts.

So what appears to be a sound horn when you start to work on it, can eventually and tragically end in broken windows, black-eyed wives and cowering dogs as it is slung out of the workshed window in all and any direction when it is found that after many hours work there is a massive hole or other flaw caused in the sheep's earlier days by the accursed fancy-type breeder.

The mature horn is, of course, the ideal one—in fact should be the only one used for the horn-headed crook. One of North England's most renowned stickmakers, Norman Tulip told me once: "We can only get good solid horn through age. We need this age and we must also have a slow growth rate." Stickmakers nowadays, he contended, were not getting access to the sound type of horns they had many years ago. The slower the growth rate, the finer becomes the texture of the horn.

Another legendary stickman, David Grant, who, when he died, left for his followers many fine examples of his work and also many helpful hints in the printed word, said a fairly large horn is needed to make a crook. It had to be fine-grained and free of cracks.

So the stickmaker has to have plenty of original horn to work with. He also requires a bench and vice which makes things a lot easier than in this writer's abode where there is a wrestling match jamming shanks and 'setting' crooks under old chairs and piling 75,000 books on top to weigh them down into shape.

The tutors at our night classes teach us first to rasp (file) off all the roughness from the horn. Then comes the heating to enable it to be set roughly to the curved shape, for it is very unlikely that the basic horn will have the desired form. Some of the old-timers boiled a turnip and shoved the horn inside it to heat. Others threw horns on an open fire or in boiling water and then forced them into shape.

Nowadays most use small heaters. My own is a paraffin lamp with a beer can for a funnel. Thisch can be exshpensive for I find it desirable to have a clean new funnel each night! Some use the camping burners and blowtorches but the experts will tell you that this heat is too fierce. What is needed is a kindly consistent warming. There are those who prefer a low flame from methylated spirits in an upturned tin lid.

Some tutors advise heating a few inches of the horn at a time, others say heat a bigger area.

Tackle on the stickmaker's bench includes a variety of clamps, metal plates and wooden blocks. If the horn is too square the head is heated and a rounded block put on the inside of the head and it is squeezed to the desired shape in the vice. Then again pieces of half-piping welded to a piece of angle-iron are used to squeeze the horn into a more compact circumference. Improvisation in tools and style is a stamp of the crookmaker.

"Patience and perseverance are essential" said David Grant. And Norman Tulip has sometimes taken 300 hours to make a crook. But he goes in for really fancy sticks including some heads which have carved horses and carts, snakes and all types of wildlife. A beef and cereal farmer in Northumberland, Norman was about to achieve his ambition of having 100 intricately-carved decorative sticks ringing the walls of one of the rooms in his home when I spent an afternoon with him.

So meticulous is he that each trout carved on a horn has the exact number, size and colour of spots as the original; each cart on his crooks has the correct fittings; and each bird—many of them hanging from delicately whittled reef knots—has the right length of feathering.

So his freezer at North Rennington, near Alnwick, had a basket full of dead wildlife and fish to make sure the finished results on the sticks he dresses are, to the best of his ability, truly representative of each species.

Norman explained to me the background to one carved head which shows a fox offering a bantam hen to his cub. "He landed in the yard one day, that fox," said Norman. "We had an awful bonnie bantie cock. B------- me, he whipped it away. I said: 'I'll do a stick on that episode.'" An excellent one it is too.

There were nearly twenty years work in Norman's collection when I visited him, mostly of intricate expressions of the everyday happenings on the land. A rabbit in a gin trap with a trailing chain; a horse and ploughman with a swing plough; a stallion attendant feeding his charge; a gypsy caravan with following ponies; Chillingham wild cattle; and a host of birds including kingfisher, curlew, sparrowhawk, teal, drake, kestrel, lapwing, magpie, golden plover, cock and hen pheasants, mallard duck, grouse, blackcock, jay and snipe.

Another stickmaker, Jimmy MacKenzie of Lockerbie, working mostly a couple of hours or so at night, can spend 100 hours on a fancy stick. He keeps pickled fish and an adder in a jar so that he too can get colours and scale exact on his ornamental crooks which have won many prizes.

We amateurs sometimes seek no more ambitious a project than a good plain stick, or even a thistle and scroll design, or a trout. David Grant once said that despite what he saw at the shows, he still preferred a plain crook. Norman Tulip reckoned that the ideal horn-headed stick should allow the user to have three fingers round the head with the other two fingers to grip it.

To make it to that stage once it has been roughly set, means a long time rasping away, rough files to begin with, progressing to smoother ones, always taking the horn out of the vice to see that the shape or angle is not being distorted. Once the material is filed off it cannot be replaced.

The head is bored with a bit—usually a half-inch bit—to take the shank which has been cut to the shape of a peg at the top. Alternatively some folk use a metal pin to go into the head and also drill at the top of the shank for the other end. Some of the modern adhesives make sure the two never part.

Bends in the shanks—which should have been cut and stored away for at least two years—are straightened after heating the offending stretch over the same small heaters. Here, the area being heated, has to be kept moist with a damp cloth to prevent it sticking or cracking.

Once shank and horn have been joined comes the more intricate work in sandpapering the horn for a smoother finish. That is, if it is a plain crook for there are many ways of carving the ornamental sticks with knives, mini-files and even cut glass. After the sandpaper it is either polish or varnish. Norman Tulip told me he used an old sock damped in a household detergent for a final polish followed by Brasso "and plenty of elbow grease." Other stickmakers use several coats of varnish and constant rubbing with sandpaper between the coats.

Varnish is also used as a seal by the makers of the show sticks who have perhaps carved grouse, fox, pheasant or trout. Here is another area where the art of secrecy comes in. Norman Tulip would not reveal to me what 'treatment' he used to bring the different types of colouring into his shanks. Nearly all his shanks are of holly which has been stripped and the 'treatment' exploits the grain in different tones which is brought up after perhaps ten or twelve years growth has been stripped off.

French polish is used by the famed stick-making family of Campbells on Mull, mainly because they became accustomed to it through their joinery business. A founder member of the Scottish Crookmakers' Association, Allister Campbell was beyond the seventy years old mark when I gained valuable hints from him on a visit to the island. Formerly from Tarbert, Loch Fyne, where he had the joinery business for thirty years, Allister started to make crooks when he was fourteen years old "and I got many a cuff on the ear for not doing it right."

His sons Allister and Iain were carrying on the business in Mull and also shared the work in producing a big number of crooks annually, many of which gain some of the country's leading show awards. "We have our own friendly arguments before we enter them for the shows," said Allister senior. "We judge them ourselves before they go, the idea being that we want to try and beat each other. We are our own biggest rivals."

Allister won forty to fifty Highland Show first prizes in his showing career. He preferred one-piece crooks, especially wooden ones. "There is a warm feel about them to the hand and if it is well made you can really be proud of it. To be really good, a crook should be as plain as possible because you have no room then even for flaws, faking or covering up. We make quite a lot of ornamental ones but I don't like it because there is a lot of gimmickry to it."

In addition to the good raw material in the horn, wood and shank Allister told me what the other essentials were—"A slice of patience and the ability to listen to good advice from well-known stickmakers."

Styles had changed little since the first shows he attended, recalled Allister. Tools were much the same too, though nowadays the files and varnishes were better.

The day before I was at their Mull homestead, the Campbells had sent 140 crooks for competition and exhibition at the Great Yorkshire Show in Harrogate. They have sent well-fashioned crooks to Canada, New Zealand, South Africa, Australia, Singapore, the U.S.A. and other countries.

Well-made crooks—not the pathetic versions you spot in touristy souvenir-selling shops at extortionate prices—go all over the world from Scotland.

CLAN MACPHERSON

*The Highlands have produced many famed farming families. Renowned
and respected fathers are often followed by sons who carry on the self-
taught attributes. The sheep and sheepdog world has quite a few of these
families. Among them are two who have gained the highest honours on
and off the trials field—Andrew MacPherson and his son Raymond.*

Even the Highland cattle were thankful for the shelter of a dykeback
from the grimmest of winter winds when I first took the snow-rutted track
deep into the Cumbrian fells to call on Raymond MacPherson, a sheepman,
who with his collies, has been linked from boyhood to vast high places.

It was no day to be abroad in that hard scrape of the 1967/68 winter.
No ingle had been as welcome for many a day as that at Tarn House,
tucked below the 2,000-odd feet of the Tindale Fell range. And Tarn
House was to continue to be a hospitable and friendly halting stop over
the years as Raymond climbed to a success which must have been far
beyond his thoughts in the days when, with his father Andrew, he
sometimes had to row six miles down a loch with his dogs to reach his car
before heading to sheepdog trials.

That was during Raymond's first sheep work near Loch Treig in
Invernesshire. We will come to the lifestyle there through his father later
in this chapter which is devoted to a family much respected and
admired—and duly honoured for being so—wherever practical hill collies
are talked about. And there are not many places where the topic fails to
arise.

Some of the sheepdog world's most coveted silverware shines
nowadays by that stretch of water at the foot of the tough, mean fells in
the north-west corner of England. They are only a few miles from the
Scottish Border, so a great temptation to those descended from the folks
who many-a-time between breakfast porridge and supper-time whisky
forayed across the boundary to grab—or rather borrow back—cattle,
sheep, wine and women.

The sheepdog honours will remain unmolested there, however, for
we Scots are content that the custodian is one of our men—a tall
Highlander thirled to sheep and collies among high Ben Nevis's mountain
skirts where he learned the craft and skill which earned him two International
Supreme Trials championships—there will be more to come—and also
the 'World' championship twice.

He came to Tarn House around 1965, and because of his residence, has to be regarded as an Englisher in the International trials world. I remember that time in 1968 he set off to the fell with nine dogs at his heel.

A good few years previously, when he was eleven years old, he had only one at his foot, the little bitch Judy, as he stalked to a trials post for the first time outside the shinty town of Newtonmore. Judy was a full sister to that great Highland character Donald MacLeod's Garry, a former Scottish Shepherd's champion.

It was in 1957 that Raymond first got his place in the Scottish team, both in the singles class and in the doubles—pair of dogs—section. Smooth-coated black and white Lark, then four years old, was the singles runner. She was a full sister to Whitehope Nap which was to feature prominently in Raymond's successes in the 1970's and so off the two McClure dogs, Glen and Meg. In the doubles or brace class Lark was partnered by old Bill, a sound herding collie bought from Jim Fleming, Cronberry, Cumnock and off two David McTeir breeders, Moss and Lassie.

Lark and Bill got Raymond into the Scottish team again in 1960 when they were second in the doubles at the National. But a leg injury to Bill cut out the International trip. Into the team again three years later, this time with his tall rough-coated Cap. Raymond was then farming a 19,000-acre hill in north Sutherland.

Cap was a sound dog off Andrew Macpherson's Mirk and Meg, Mirk being a grandson of J. M. Wilson's Moss and going back paternally to Wilson's Tweed. Another Wilson's Mirk dog, Ben, was there at Tarn House in the late 60's when the byre was lined with collies including trials winners, Shep and Tweed.

I also saw the smooth-haired alert 1½-year-old Nap, the only short-haired collie on the bleak fell farm. He was off Raymond's Ben out of T. Graham's Jill, a Whitehope Nap daughter. I described Nap on that visit as a sound and powerful looking worker but did not realise that a few years later he would come right to the brim. I saw him win the English National Championship at Middlesborough in 1971—that was a great victory for Scotland on enemy territory—and also two years later thrill sheepmen from many nations in the heat of east-coast America when he won the first-ever so-called 'World' championship.

Another of my calls to Tarn House was in the winter of 1973 when Nap was still in quarantine after that memorable trip to the U.S.A. On a grey-blue afternoon I walked with Raymond at his sheep work, seeing his dog Tweed just visible more than a mile away heading for the black heather ground to seek Swaledale-blooded Blackfaces.

Only a few, maybe a score, had dallied by the old broken dyke on the banking beyond the bog and would need turned out to the heights of Cold Fell when found by Tweed, guided by a fusion of commands, brain and initiative. "He'll go on until he finds them," said Raymond, who is not for letting the Blackfaces lie at the bottom of the hills at night and had in his years on the rough Cumbrian fell ground, tutored the ewes to return to the tops in the mid-afternoon.

So Tweed, distant but purposeful and on Raymond's long-stretching fell rakes only because he had biff and sting for a dog-sized chore, got going with push behind the sheep, most of which turned out to be gimmers—young ewes—a bit lazy at raking their ground, so still in need of a hunt out.

Up the pad surged the laggers, some of the 1,390 ewes Raymond had at the time at Tarn House. A gliff through the binoculars and then another piercing wheep of commands from an outstanding whistler who had made them heard that year from Pennsylvania to Llanfairfechan. On a still afternoon they carried well over the former tin mining hamlets on the other side. In fact, on such a day, there is no knowing where the dirl of the whistle would peter out.

There were three collies at our heels that day, Tweed who was used in the long runs, eleven-year-old Lyn and six year old Bess. Tweed, then a 3½ year old son of John Gilchrist's Spot and out of Jim Wannon's Bess, and a runner-up for the Welsh championship in 1972 when owned by Alan Jones, was called eventually to heel. He had returned twice to the bottom for more distant ewes—a fair mileage in under an hour. "It is far too much for a young dog to do a run of that distance," said Raymond. "But Tweed is a good all-round dog and can save me an awful lot of work. If he could not go for those sheep, I would be away down there still crawling about at the bottom."

So old Lyn gratefully took over to edge the bulk farther out as we got to a lirk at the back of the fell. Daughter of Lloyd's Garry, the 1962 International supreme champion and out of a daughter of J. M. Wilson's old Bill, she swung back and forth across the big load of ewes effortlessly and there was no slacking. It is an impressive sight to see bulk move freely, yet with consideration.

"I have a feeling things are not being done in a practical way at some trials," said Raymond. "I think work is getting too slow. It is not going at quick enough a pace. I can never see a good run when the sheep are grazing or stopped. Sheep should be moving all the time. If you are judging you should be harder on dogs that you can see are lacking power if they are continually asked to come on. The job should be done in a practical way. If you put your dog out for sheep, you expect him to go for them and bring them with purpose. When I'm judging I look for a good practical run. I like them to show power and command over sheep. There is a happy medium—a practical pace with the sheep moving all the time.

"Quite a few of the dogs lack a bit of sting and power today. On three or four sheep they might be making a wonderful job, but when they get bulk they sometimes run into difficulties. They will have to get more of Whitehope Nap blood. He had sting, power and guts and I don't think we should go far away from that strain."

That brought the crack back to his 'World' champion Nap as we

70

returned from the fell. "There are many who would find a dog like him hard to handle, but his enthusiasm for his work is something which has stood me in good stead, both on the hill and trials fields. I always enjoy working a dog that has something in reserve. Once you have mastered them and built up an understanding—they are impetuous until about four years of age—you have a dog that will stand a tremendous amount of work and this is the type I prefer."

As Tweed drew nearer his heels—this dog too was to head for America and retain Raymond's 'World' title three years later—he said: "I like to see a pup that has a bit of devil in him. If they are too nice and refined I don't think they turn out best. But if you have a pup with a bit of go and determination and individuality you have got something to work on.

"If I saw a young dog and he was not registered (with the International Sheep Dog Society, the governing body for collie registrations) I would not hesitate to buy it if I saw he was a really good one. He would have to have guts and enthusiasm for his job. Some of the unregistered dogs have real power."

Just before heading back to the farmhouse Raymond cast out the young dog which that year gained him a place in the English team, a half white-faced eager collie called Zac. He was sent nearly a mile down the glen to hunt up to the tops the few Blackies which had not drawn up on their own accord. "I may never win the International championship," mused Raymond "but this is the only way to get a chance at all—to run the dogs on ground like this on all-round work."

Zac leapt into the Land Rover after his work. Less than two years later at four and a half years old the black and white collie was surrounded by the magnificent collection of silverware which goes to an International champion as, over the bare-cropped racecourse at York, he helped steer Raymond to his first supreme victory in the blue-riband of the sheepdog world.

York is still remembered for some brilliant shepherding in the supreme championship on the final day for it followed some rather dreary Internationals in the previous years. Zac had been purchased by Raymond to keep up his working team strength while Nap and his other collie Speed were in quarantine following the 1973 U.S.A. trip.

Raymond was undoubtedly proud of his U.S.A. victory with Nap but I have no hesitation in thinking that the supreme championship victory over the flat York course with Greyface sheep which were free moving and kindly when in bigger droves, rightly gave him the biggest thrill of his sheepdog life. Again this collie has the classical Whitehope Nap line. Off Fred Coward's Ken and John Hadwin's Queen he goes back paternally to Tot Longton's famed old Rob, John Gilchrist's Bob, Robert Fraser's sound Mindrum Nell, to Jim Gilchrist's Spot and more of the Mindrum Rob and old Nell blood plus Welsh infusion of R. L. Jones' Lad and T. W. O. Jones'

71

Tot. Maternally he is a grandson of another grand International supreme, Llyr Evans' Bosworth Coon and has the strain of J. M. Wilson's great breeder, Bill 11, a son of Whitehope Nap out of J. C. Howie's Meg.

It was blood which became very much in demand after that York victory. Zac had proved a trials champion of worth. If there is any doubt about that it can be dispelled immediately by the thoughts of handlers from other U.K. nations when the time of the National events—at which the teams for the International earn their places—comes round. If Zac was in the English team, then that was the one to beat.

He proved this in 1979 when he again climbed to the top rung in the International Trials on its first visit to Galloway at Stranraer. Alas, my change of occupation meant I was unable to see this further triumph for Raymond but there will be future times when I expect to see the tall Highlander achieve the victory again.

These International wins must have red rings round them on the Tarn House diary. So too must 16 June 1979. Over the parkland at Rouken Glen in Glasgow in a gathering of International handlers, Raymond piloted Zac to yet another major prize.

On the same day it was announced that he had been awarded the M.B.E. in the Queen's Birthday Honours list—fitting reward for a career in which he has proved at home and overseas in his trialing, judging and practical sheep work, a great ambassador for the pastoral world.

And on that same day as he was gaining that double dose of success, his father Andrew who first leaned his crook against a sheepdog trial post fifty-nine years previously with a ten-shilling bitch at his foot, added another notch to his championship record at Tomatin trials in Inverness-shire.

Andrew, by that time, had come off the high remote places. No more was there that eight mile walk with his dogs from the homestead to the nearest place where he could park his car beyond Loch Treig, cradled away in the vast mountains between Lochaber and Rannoch.

No more either making that long trip on the single-track fifty miles from Fort William to the north shore of the limb known as Ardnamurchan Peninsula.

"If I was younger I would not have left that country, but it is tough going now on the hills for gathering," said Andrew to me in 1971 when I visited him in his 'retirement' home, an eighty-six-acre mixed farm on the outskirts of Dornoch. He has since moved further down the hill to Glenferness, Nairn.

These must have been vivid days 'herding the steep hills and seeking with his son Raymond, the Blackfaces above Loch Treig. Andrew was tenant there of 4,000-acres with a carry of 1,000 ewes and 250 hoggs, "Sometimes there were just the two of us and sometimes another shepherd gave us a hand. You had to go quietly for the sheep were wild and would bolt into the rocks. If you whistled or made a noise they were off. So we

72

had to have very quiet trial dogs for that job. . . good wide-working dogs.

"The hoggs were wintered on the hill and were never speaned. (Weaned from their mothers). It was a different way of handling sheep altogether. There were certain parts of the ground it paid you to stop off the hill at lambing time in case the sheep were frightened and went into the burns or left their lambs. You could do more harm than good.

"We needed good dogs for the gatherings for the sheep were going so hard. They only settled down when they got into big numbers.

"The storms were generally not too bad. We never had big losses apart from one year when we had only twenty-eight per cent lambing—twenty-eight lambs per 100 ewes—because of the weather. But the sheep thrived. It was the wool we depended on up there. This was what we were after all the time—there was never really a big crop of lambs as there were so many drawbacks like foxes, burns and hoodie crows."

When attending trials Andrew and Raymond sometimes had to leave home at 5 a.m. to walk the eight miles to near Tulloch where their car was parked. Or sometimes boated six miles down the loch with the dogs and returned in the early hours of the next morning.

These were dogs which had to run to just under 4,000 ft in that high territory where Andrew stayed for fourteen years before buying 4,000 acres at Achateny in Ardnamurchan. From 1962 to 1969 he tended 1,200 Blackface ewes, 300 ewe hoggs and 167 head of cattle.

But the fascinating life of one of the north's most respected handlers began many, many years before even the Loch Treig days, though that station at Tulloch had something to do with it.

Andrew is a Strathspey man and in his early teens he was one of the ten-shilling a week shepherds of that airt who took on the droving of hoggs across to airts such as Banffshire for wintering. Strathspey was then the land of the half beardie—"good all-round dogs"—and there were few trials collies.

On his travels to the Nairn land he once came across a crofter's bitch having difficulty in crossing a frozen burn. He noticed that the bitch had whelped and asked her owner—"Will you keep me a pup?" "Will ten shillings be too much?" queried the crofter. "No," said Andrew and eventually a pup, to be named Lark, was his.

Andrew still has a programme from the 1920 Kingussie sheepdog trials. There were just under twenty entries, among them Andrew MacPherson and Lark. He was fifteen years old then, and it was the first trial he had ever seen.

The following year he missed the event because Lark had pups that day. The next year, however, he went back with Lark and her pup Vic to only the second trial he had seen. He won the Inverness-shire Sheepdog Trials Association cup with Vic and was third with Lark. The following year he won the cup outright being first with Trix and fourth with Bess. Also with Bess he was fifth in the open class, the first North countryman

73

to win a place in that esteemed section for it was then dominated by the more famous men from the south.

These dogs were to take part in the droving of hoggs from West to East. They included wanders like the one when he took over 300 hoggs at Tulloch Station and walked them for about ten days before reaching their wintering quarters at Knockando.

He has returned many times to Kingussie which by 1925-26 was drawing some sixty dogs including the best in Britain. Bagshaw, Telfer, Priestley, Thorpe and Wallace were some of the south men up to seek the silverware but they were up against it with Scottish characters of the mettle of Sandy Millar, J. M. Wilson, Tom Dickson and others.

Andrew, like another of the northmen from about the same period, Donald MacLeod of Bonar Bridge, went in for ghillie work for several years. He did lambings too, before acquiring his own eighty-acres in Strathspey. Then a 'herding spell again before going to Loch Treig.

That loch certainly helped to kit out a family well for the dog trials world.

TOOL OF THE TRADE

Scotland's landscape gets a hammering each day from one of the most essential means of propulsion—the hill boot. Like the dog and the crook it is an emblem of the upland farmer and the shepherd with its distinctive shape and its upturned nose.

It was the combustion engine which knocked the feet from the hill men.

The Gnat vehicle, they will tell you, can manage the near-straight-up inclines; the Haflinger can stoor up an old drove track like a midge. Watch too the Snow-Trics and Tracs buck up and over white-topped ditches and heather in many an airt while the Muskeg Bombadier trips lightly, though heavily laden, across deep bog and fast flowing water.

There is also that jack-of-all trades, the Land Rover, undaunted by the steep, and her rural companion, the Gypsy. And in this new decade a plethora of similarly-rigged oriental and continental counterparts. All mechanical aids you might think to bring the flockmaster and his shepherd these two well-bandied words, economy and viability.

But for many a long while before they spluttered onto bent-grass and bracken, something else kept the hill men on their feet—hill buits. The hill buit—the upland sheepman's classic stamp of trade—ever-searching the skies with its upturned nose alert as a ferret emerging from a set, can never be equalled for its purpose by anything the engineers, the technocrats and the boffins can construct.

The Land Rover cannot go where the hill buit will stoutly and safely carry its master. And the ski-tracked two-strokes will never clamber or trek the pads which the hill buit strides majestically.

The helicopter was also considered. But it has not the initiative or the guile of the buit when winter puts her mist shawls on the slopes of sheepland. Even the Japanese have tried to knock the feet off our outbye flockmen whose hefty and gleg footwear is capable of deeds far beyond number. They have jiggered about with their Yamasukihonda motorbikes, kitting them with knobbly tyres and sheep-reassuring quiet exhausts to help the shepherd stalk his scoreage of Blackie or Cheviot. But they forgot to fit a receptacle for his crook. And they were not able either to imitate the music that is composed as a hand-made buit climbs the inch-wide pads of the hillsides. So the Nips will not manage a mechanical rival. Maybe having discovered they cannot do so, they will turn to the obvious answer—to copy the hill buit itself.

But traditional craftsmen who make the purpose-built shepherd's boot among their noisy world of skivers, clickers, closers, bends and kip tongues are now as scarce as red-furred moles in an igloo.

Their skill and patience—they can perhaps make between six and eight pair a week—fashions not only an item that is friendly, noisy and acceptable on every market day in our townships (except to those whose role is the upkeep of our pavements) but a unique pastoral implement-cum-vehicle-cum-tool.

The hill buit can douse a moorland fire. Its 6 lbs. or so of weight can make any obstinate black hill cow move. It can realign a sagging dyke if struck accurately and with care, mind you, for it has five inhabitants.

Travelling at least 4 m.p.h. over the uneven kinks of our sheep hills, it will take shepherd or flockmaster through bog and burn and any combination of geographical feature for a lifetime of about two years before needing re-shod.

The hill buit, sometimes built on full-sprung lasts that give a three-inch spring, helped give birth to the shepherd's legendary stride. No townie boot can climb the sheepground that they daily tackle with freedom and gusto. Hill buits have never been bettered—not even by the Chieftain tank—for deterring the accursed tourist off the pavements on market day. And for clearing the way forward in a crowded bar when time is short and only three pints before closing.

They have been perfected for their many decades of existence with a navigation system whose homing ability has not even been equalled by the likes of the Apollo space vehicles. There are many, many herds who will testify to this for they have been steered faithfully back to their cottar homes regularly from lamb sales, tup fairs, sheepdog trials 'herds suppers and sundry events where one has of necessity to partake of medicinal relief for the weight one carries on his feet.

I foresee the day soon when the ever-growing clutch of conservation societies will gird up their flower-power and protest that the hill buit is destroying the common daisy. They—the buits, not the conservationists—are harmless, and also a benefit to nature even when their days are done and, steel-stiff and toothless, they are discarded. Thrown into the hedge or stuffed into a dyke, they are cosy and protective homes for the songbirds come nesting time.

Cats have had kittens in many a hill buit. The byre window can be brightened with flowers straggling out of the buit's remnants. Billy Connolly's wellies have only a fraction of the uses to which a hill buit can be put.

Those of us whose Sunday night chores used to be to run to the barn and cut fresh straw to 'bed' the family's buits and clogs for the next week, can still recall the tang of dubbin and oils which brought the buits softness and wearability. There were the jokers who, seeing us coggling along on new buits, would call: "Buits, where are ye gaun wi' the boy?"

76

Many cottage folk today own two pair of hill buits with one pair recuperating soaked in home-mixed oil concoctions including castor oil and even sheep carcase grease, while the others are in use. Hill buits mean nearly one hundred per cent freedom from bunions and corns. A once famed flockman, Jamie Scott—'Troneyhill' they called him in his heyday at sheepdog trials—boasted: "If you have a pair of watertight hill buits you don't need socks."

I have heard when visiting the noted bootmakers, Thomas Rogerson and Sons of Galashiels who have been making hill buits since 1905, that there was an Innerleithen shepherd who took a size 18. When I did a feature on his firm in 1969 Jack Rogerson told me that their hill buit was made as near as possible to the old hand-made original design. Reducing the weight could shorten the life of a buit, said Mr Rogerson who claimed the drift from the land has a profound effect on production and sales of the upland footwear.

The intriguing part of the hill buit is its cocked nose. Origin of the style is uncertain but Mr Rogerson thought the 'lift' was originally regional to the Scottish borders or was probably developed in Dumfries and Galloway. Hill buits have gone from Galashiels to the U.S.A. and Canada and one day at Lockerbie market a young Scots emigrant called at the firm's stance and took three pair.

Nine years after my visit to Gala, amid the clank of the clicking press, the whirr of a skiver and other machinery that was up to 100 years old, I watched Dick Goudie, backed by fifty-one years experience, fashioning hill buits in his crammed Maybole workshop.

Dick was one of the last remaining traditional manufacturers. He had started making them when they were twenty-five shillings a pair. At the time of my call they would be costing £40 but you can add another ten or twenty pounds to that now.

At one time Dick could recall ten boot-making factories in the Ayrshire town. He reckoned, like Mr Rogerson, that the hill buit has not changed in appearance much over the years. "It is something that no-one has asked to be altered. You might get people who want tackets put in a different way, that is about all. Some like them in rows, some in groups of three, or some in a half-moon shape."

What has changed, however, was the cost, and difficulties sometimes in finding good raw material to make the quality job on which Dick always insisted. Leather was hit hard by inflation, tackets were on the scarce side and oiled thread was getting difficult to obtain.

Dick's constant shepherding visitors left him various hints on maintenance of the buits. Normally he reckoned a pair of buits could last twelve to fifteen months before needing repairs. But on soft hill ground they can last longer. Before a new set left his workshop Dick made them waterproof with melted dubbin brushed along all the seams.

He knew one shepherd who was prepared to have damp feet for a month until his constant rubbing with dubbin sealed them.

"I always asked the shepherds what they used to keep their boots in order. They all have different tricks handed down from grandfathers or from older shepherds," said Dick. "One man in Northumberland used to keep three pair of boots and he filled them with castor oil and hung them up until the oil came through. He then took them down, emptied out the oil and said that after walking for five minutes on the hill the boots would fit perfectly to the shape of his feet."

The humble but practical hill buit, has been duly recognised by the shepherd-poets. Here is a sample from farmer Joe Johnstone, Garrieston, Dunscore, Dumfriesshire.

Trysted Hill Boots.

When the embers burn low and the telly goes dead
    The time it is late and maist folks in bed
And we sit there in silence, as silent as mutes
    There comes to my mind my first trysted boots.

From the far days of yore they step to my dreams
    To remind me of youth and long ago scenes
Of valleys and burns where I guddled for troots
    Of friends who are gone that wore trysted hill boots.

When I was a laddie I toddled in clogs
    Wi' bag and wi' stick and black and white dogs
At markings, at clippings, at speanings and shoots
    I envied the 'herds in their high-sprung hill boots.

The left and the right on a brown paper sheet
    Wearing hand knitted socks I pencilled my feet
Two strings round the insteps and tied into loops
    For that was the size of my first trysted boots.

Six long weary months I did patiently kill
    When the down-laden postman came over the hill
With unmeasured joy my heart jumped in fits
    For the package he bore was my first trysted buits.

No monarch his kingdom surveyed with more pride
    No artist so proudly his painting has eyed
The twinkle-toed suedes worn by long-haired galoots
    Were never so smart as my new trysted boots.

Two half semi-circles designed in the tacks
    With plates at the fronts and plates at the backs
The perfumes from Paris or priceless cheroots
    Could ne'er smell so sweet as my new trysted boots.

Wi' lang even strides I tended my flocks
  The tags stuck behind like the spurs of gamecocks
The gay feathered peafowl, the satin dressed rooks
  Had nothing on me in my new trysted boots.

When tramping through snaw or flachtering peat
  T'was grand to review the marks o' yer feet
At stock valuations or Whitsunday flits
  I was never wantin' my high sprung hill buits.

At lamb sales I sat on my pen's topmost bar
  Wi' lang shankit stick, fashioned figures in glaur
As there I sat feeding on sweeties and fruits
  The folk that were passing admired my hill boots.

Some fellows play football, some like sailing boats
  Some fellows play cricket, some sow their wild oats
There's others prefer to sook whisky frae stroops
  My delight is in dogs and high sprung hill boots.

No blemish from bunion, no scar left by corn
  No ingrowing nails that require to be shorn
No down-fallen arches but perfect placed toots
  It's thanks to broad welts and high sprung hill boots.

If footwear have spirits that Peter enrolls
  There must be in heaven two cheery old 'soles'
And there when I join them to harps or to flutes
  I'll dance jigs and reels in my high sprung hill boots.

But if for my sins and my crimes upon earth
  I'm sentenced to serve in the underworld berth
I ask first one favour, dear Satan, auld cloots
  Can I daunder roon hell in my high sprung hill boots?

SKYWARDS TO THE DOGS

Going to the dogs had oftimes, in many households, led to 'family discussions.' Those of us afflicted by the ailment of 'sheepdogtrialitis' have been known to stravaig from home late of a Friday night, sleep overnight in the car, or stir around 3 a.m. on a Saturday morning and hie to a trials field many county-lengths away. Some times it can be halfway round the world.

One shepherd speaking at a social was once asked: "What is a sheep dog trial?" "Well," he replied, "I got the perfect answer last week when a' dunted ma wife in the ribs at three o'clock in the mornin' and askit her if she wid make me up a piece and a flask fur a' wis heedin' off tae a dog trial, but a' hed better no repeat her description o' a trial in this company."

Those of us whose lifemode sometimes entails rising just after midnight and arriving back beyond the following midnight from such shepherding occasions, are not to be envied.

I have also flown off to see dogmen at work in the States, in Nova Scotia and deep into a wondrous land 'down under.' Not many can say they went 12,000 miles to see a man about a dog.

But in 1975 down country from the valleys of sprouting geysers I saw descendants of old Scottish settlers' dogs barking loud and long to thrust Romney sheep up a 2,000 ft mountain top over Ngongotaha. Sun-weathered ever-smiling Maoris from the likes of Ranginwahia, Waipukarau, Te Kuiti, Ngaruawahia and Putorino commanded black and tans, brindles, quarter beardies and grizzlies on the steep slope to show the power which is harnessed daily in the high parts of New Zealand, a necessity in mustering the mobs of that country's most valuable resource.

Below on the valley bottom within sight of the wonders of thermal Rotorua and its boiling mud, heading dogs, including some whose previous duties had been with cattle and sheep in Wales and Yorkshire and even on an Australian rice farm, displayed their worth in close sheep work.

It all ended in a cliffhanger at the New Zealand International Expo' '75 Championship trials which provided six memorable days of shepherding a 1,300 ewe tally—a mere mini-fraction of this faraway land's sixty million sheep count.

They were strong, calm sheep at Ngongotaha, wool-headed Romneys and shorter-legged clean-faced Perendales, which the Huntaway dogs on the mountain trials course and the heading dogs on the showfield in front of a hillful of several thousand spectators dealt with in seeking the tempting prizes at the Expo' event. This was the second one to include British contestants.

Bob Wilson, gentlest of handlers and a legend in New Zealand, carefully and deservedly 'herded his slim prick-eared bitch Rose to a points tally which ensured the heading section victory rostrum and a magnificent jade-mounted trophy. Then seventy-two years old and from Kirwee country twenty miles south of Christchurch in the south island, Bob had lost count of his wins away back in 1967. But by that time they had totalled 1,000.

Bill Taylor, slightly behind Bob Wilson in experience for he had only thirty-eight years at trialling, compared to the doyen's fifty, cajolled his black ten year old toughie Rock to bark and back his way to the Huntaway championship.

The Huntaway is the specialist noisy dog—now in the UK—without which the huge spreads of rough, bush, back and hill country of New Zealand could not be mustered. Their role too is at yarding work be it at mart, wool shed or freezer works where they bound along the backs of the sheep to clear jammed pens.

They possibly originated with the beardie dogs of our own rock-dotted north-west Scotland, going out with early settlers and being developed and tailored to their new environment by the likes of the McIntyre family, one of whose decendants, I met at the New Zealand event.

Some say the Kiwis put in a touch of Labrador and Harrier for more noise and moulded them to the finished article which comes in various hues and coats and which is unequalled there on the tussock, scrub, mountain and yard. There were many worthies among the Huntaway men with several Maori handlers among them working dogs with names like Joe Savoldi, McMillan, Pedro, Nigger, Rogue and York.

One of them was a Maori with some Scottish blood. 'Dubby' Powers (his real name is Henry James) grabbed the headlines after the first day in the heading championship. "My grandfather was a half-caste Irishman and my grandmother a half-caste Scot," said Dubby who ran a 750-acre sheep and cattle unit near Wairarapa.

Another character who made a big hit at the event was a former Argyllshire shepherd who has been in the Southern Hemisphere for about twenty years and was running probably one of the world's only team of red and white Border Collies.

Duncan McGillivray, whose accent was still as broad as his name, did a good deal of collie exhibition work as well as competing at trials. He shepherded on the Noble family's sheep ground at Ardkinglas in Argyll before going to Australia in 1956 as a stud shepherd with Corriedale stock near Gelong in Victoria.

While there, some red pups appeared, from a mating of black and white collies and he stuck to the colour since then. In 1975 Duncan was leasing a 200-acre unit with a Perendale sheep stud at South Wairarapa in the North Island. During the Expo' event he gave an excellent demonstration with his red and white collies. He told me then: "Some day I'll get a visit back to Scotland." Alas, I missed him when he did come over on holiday in 1979 and visited the Scottish National trials in his home county of Argyll.

Another Scot, this time a lady, challenged the champions during the event. Mrs Margaret McCoward who left Aberdeen in 1951 had never seen a sheepdog trial in Scotland before she left. Yet from her 1½-acre home at Taradale in Hawkes Bay she regularly entered trials and obedience competitions with her collies and had gained twenty prizes in thirteen trials.

The British entrants at that 1975 event found the trials courses vastly different from our own. John Evans of Wales took fourth place. The other UK handler was Allan Heaton from Yorkshire.

There was little time for sight-seeing in New Zealand. I admired the Aberdeen Angus and the wool shed set-up of Donald Urquhart at Papakura not far from Auckland. Donald had been a visitor to Scottish trials several years previously and it was in his home that I watched a film of one of Scotland's best-ever collies, Thomson McKnight's Drift which he had 'shot' with his camera when on the UK visit.

After the Expo Trials I set off for Palmerston North with another Kiwi who had been a keen trials visitor during his stay in this country, Bob Mather. We shared the driving of a bouncing farm utility pick-up truck around 150 desperate miles on a dusty, untarred interior bush road through Urewera National Park as we headed for his home.

Amid the deafening chorus of secadda insects among the pochutukawa trees in the massed bush we halted at a Maori settlement, the only signs of civilisation we had seen for hours. And when the stoorie trip consists of six or seven hours without a bite to eat, a couple of pies from the sell-everything store in that rare bush break can whack your Gleneagles or Wimpy fare any day.

Heads of wild pigs adorned the store wall. Skins of the 'possum testified to their big population in the area. A Maori shepherd cantered past on horseback, possibly the youngest mode of travel thereabouts, for any four-wheeled vehicles were buckled and aged, though serviceable.

It is queer where the oddities of life can land a soul when heading for a sheepdog trial. For, courtesy of British Airways, there were halts in Dubai, Singapore, Doha, Brisbane and on the return leg Melbourne and Beirut. Tantalising glimpses too over India, Bali, the Persian Gulf, Turkey, Bulgaria and Yugoslavia. And sitting at Auckland International Airport I looked at enticing places such as Tonga, Papeete, Landi, the Norfolk Islands and Nukualofa.

I had hoped to visit the South Island of New Zealand but arrangements fell through. The aim had been to call on some of the far back-country mustering men who figure so much in the Kiwi land's colourful sheep history with their dogs and their legends. It is a land which needs another visit.

A couple of years previously and out of the blue I had been asked if I would like a free plane ticket to attend the first-ever 'World' championship sheepdog trial in the U.S.A. and a memorable gathering of sheepdogmen from several nations it turned out to be. But it ended sadly. It had been so cheery, so rewarding among the genial folk of other countries over three days in the tree-clothed countryside of East-coast America. We had seen Raymond MacPherson, Highlander from the stiff fell pads of Cumbria, majestically capture the massive championship honours after hard toil with his black Nap, starting in the mushroom country of Pennsylvania, continuing under the gaze of turkey buzzards in Maryland and ending amid the deafening dirl of massed pipe bands after a trio of skin-scorching days.

We also followed his closest challenger, Ayrshire farmer John Templeton, the previous year's International Trials champion, in a never-say-die bid which brought him the runners-up place with black and white Fleet.

The two Britons with their four collies gaining four out of the first five prizes in the big dollar-and-silver shareout earned us the team award. And just to make it an all-Scots affair at the brim, the other handler in that first handful was young Jackie Knox, one-time tender of Gilmanscleugh Blackies in Ettrick and at that time on Columbia-Ramboullet ewes in North Carolina, a state twice the size of Scotland.

There was much more too. The stetsons and high boots and humour of the U.S. men and their friendly families, the colourful rig-outs and commands of South Africa's respected handler and the popular lads from Canada who were maybe bottom of the points total but tops in cheeriness.

Then suddenly, just when farewells were being said to the far-scattered sheepmen and we were trying to say thanks for the hospitality, came word that our motel several miles away and where the collies had been left, was ablaze. In the late night, happiness turned to heartbreak. John Templeton's Fleet—seen only a few hours earlier by a well-filled grandstand in a demonstration which was to be John's last work with the eight year old collie and his partner Cap following their purchase by Fred Bahnson of North Carolina—died in the smoke. So too, did two collies of that Texan character Pope Robertson. Others, including those of Raymond MacPherson, were fortunate to survive.

No one was injured and for that we were thankful. But grief can have many forms. What would have been a triumphant return—and it was not easy for our lads to win the booty—was a quiet one. Nevertheless the honours were taken and worthily merited, under a controversial decision-making system laid out for the event. It was substituting a system of computership for stockmanship. It was ironed out a bit three years later, when another 'World' trial was held and Raymond MacPherson again took the top award.

The gathering of Britons, Americans, Canadians and South Africans at that 1973 event was as cheery a company as you will find anywhere. They had all been names prior to that, names which appeared through the post weekly in the deluge of letters which came in from subscribers to the monthly *Scottish Sheepdog Handler* which went out from this house for seven toiling years before Old Father Time decreed that the workload was too heavy.

There was no spare time during the visit. There were evening barbecues and functions before it all began; then sometimes 6 a.m. get-togethers to reach distant trials courses. There was hefty, solid rain and the threat of tornadoes. Then there were five or six days of scalding sunshine.

Those of us whose natural herbage on top is giving way to open parkland were extremely grateful for the use of the protective hats of whatever kind and shape we sometimes appeared in.

We saw hovering turkey buzzards and a white egret. Others saw groundhogs and black snakes. There were thousands of Santa Gertrudi cattle on the massive Buck and Doe Run Valley farm. There were Angus herds and Cheviot flocks. Visits to Holstein herds ranged from some of the most modern layouts in the U.S.A. to a couple who still hauled in silage in a barrow and had the biggest beasts we saw. And they were the happiest of the lot.

There were turnpikes, freeways and endless highways. Dozens and dozens of busy petrol stations despite the reported fuel shortage at the time. And Raymond MacPherson and John Templeton knocked back the motor lodge skyscraper Strawberry Sundaes like Dolly Mixtures.

Their wives Margaret and May were thrilled by all the hospitality. So too, of course, were the other British visitors and their wives. For above all, it was probably the personal contact which made it all so memorable. Not the cities, the traffic, the trials course, or the general American way of life. But the personalities and how they all got on together.

We had heard of Pope Robertson before. A feed merchant from Texas, he had been to the fore for many years. But we did not know he was such a character—gum swollen with plug tobacco and a megaphone in his hand he was a real sight at the trials post. He reckoned he was able to command the dogs at half a mile with the megaphone. Alas, his two collies died in the motor lodge blaze.

Then there was Jim McEwen. Just another name before. Now we got to know him as a livewire, high-steppin' it at the square dance which followed a welcoming barbecue the evening before the World Trial started. Jim Dewbre from Texas was another name we had known from trials results. Here was a character straight out of the 'High Noon' era. A preacherman who showed us one day how to make a lynching noose. He was also an excellent country and western singer.

There were the Pulfer families from Ohio—Lewis and Ralph. Brian Nettleton who drove 1,200 miles from Nova Scotia—an Englishman married to a Scots girl and a non-stop humourist. Near the tail-end of the 1970's he and his charming family were my very hospitable hosts when I spent sometime on a sheep story in Nova Scotia and Prince Edward Island.

Ron Philip and Rodney Miles brought the South African accent and their wives. They also brought tales of their farming in the southern part of that land. Ron was running 1,200 Merino sheep while Rodney on his 2,700 acres at that time had ewes and 100 Friesland cows.

There were many others whose kindnesses and hospitality we all appreciated. They came in caravettes, tents and in campers—the piggie-back mobile homes which fit on the back of pick-up trucks.

Arthur Allan from Illinois was another personality—I saw him win the U.S.A. championship just before the 'World' joust with his imported bitch, Fleet, a daughter of John Gilchrist's Spot. One of the all-time greats in the U.S.A. trials world he had started trialling in 1939 with a Scots-blooded dog and by 1973 had imported around 200 collies.

He has given demonstrations at such exotic abodes as the Snake River Stampede, Spanish Trails Fiesta, Pioneer Day Celebration Rodeo, Tulsa, Durango, Baton Rouge—strange, strange Zane Grey locales for a man and his dog. He had featured in shows and films with Roy Rogers, Gene Autrey and Walt Disney.

Arthur sometimes drove 2,000 miles to a trial. One of his finest-ever collies for film work was the prick-eared black Nicky. He starred in Walt Disney's "Arizona Sheepdog." With special training he was able to handle chipmunks and mountain lions in one of the films in which he starred. His Rock, a bonnily marked dog, was for six years undefeated champion at all official trials sponsored by the North American Sheepdog Society. Born in 1948 off John Gilchrist's supreme International champion Bob, he went to Illinois at eighteen months of age and I have a feeling I have seen somewhere that one of his exhibitions was in front of 102,000 people.

Among the busiest folks at that 1973 event were Bill and Tibbie McMichael who brought their wheeled mobile home from Ontario. To we Britons it became a five-star catering establishment with tea on the hour, the half-hour and even in between. Though he had gone from Dumfriesshire twenty-two years earlier, Bill still baffled us with some of his Dumfriesshire words.

Such gatherings do no harm.

THE ISLAND DWELLERS

Folk fairly make an island. In the beauteous west of our land there are such people and such places. My work fortunately took me to some of these gems—Muck, Mull, Ulva, Coll, Gigha and Kerrera. Some only lie a whisper-width from the mainland, others many boatlengths over the heaving waters. But all maintain their individuality.

Many things make an island. There is the timelessness which comes especially late at night such as on a three-day working visit to Muck, bobbing a long way offshore past Dubh Sgier's razor-backed guard to the ridged isle's pier, pulling in glinting saithe and lythe fish.

There are more materialistic things too, though much less than in the city, and perhaps a good thing too. Like on Muck at that time in 1976—four phones, one mile of road, sixty gates, unique top heavy dykes, more than 600 ewes, sixty-five cows and nine ponies. And to cap it all on the low, green, 1,600-acre 2½-mile long isle, twenty or so people with a fine leavening of skills, personalities and experiences.

We had gone to the land, seven miles adrift of Ardnamurchan Point, and a member of the Small Isles, for a story on Lawrence MacEwen's farming set-up. His family farmed the entire acreage, shipping off lambs to Kinross and rearing calves, either for the store trade or home over-wintering.

Problems though, mostly connected with transport and economics, can be surmountable or appear to be so when you have folk with the cheeriness of Lawrence's mother, Mrs Edith MacEwen, Charlie MacDonald, Jessie MacRae and some of the younger folk who were then making a go of things. Mrs MacEwen had just finished revising the *Isle of Muck Cookery Book* when I was on her proud little land. The booklet included about 60 recipes. Once a lecturer in zoology she was then making her own bread at Gallanach Farm for her sons Lawrence and Ewen. A fine sight it was to see her cheerily at work.

Back in the early 1800's there were some 280 crofters on the isle, according to the guide book compiled by Lawrence who found himself in the headlines in 1979 when he wed a girl from another near-hand isle, Soay. Charlie MacDonald was keeping the crofting tradition going near the little port when photographer Niall Robertson and I were there.

Charlie had started work on the estate among Clydesdales when he was fourteen years old and had completed fifty-four years service, a masterly example of loyalty. He could recall there being five Clydesdales on the farm and he had many jovial stories to tell of taking Blackfaces across to the Salen show in the island's launch—and in bringing them back! Sometimes as many as fifteen sheep were taken and his collection of prize tickets included some for the best wool at the event in 1974 and 1948. A dram does not last long when a soul gets involved with this sort of recollection.

Charlie had worked tractors since the first one was landed on Muck around 1950 but he still proudly pointed to a picture in a book showing the last of the island's Clydesdales grubbing cabbages in 1962. Never dissatisfied with his work, he told me he never had any thoughts of leaving the isle.

One thing he and his Uist-born wife had on the isle was a braw grand-daughter, Sheena, then eleven-months-old. We stayed with Sheena's parents, Bruce and Sandra Mathers and their hospitality and kindness and crack is something you will not find in today's motelling era. A one-time tax inspector, Bruce did most of the arable and tractor work on the farm and also had occasional duties with the cargo launch. He married Sandra—definitely one of the isle's best cooks—in the farm's barn. For the occasion, the island was weighed down by 160 visitors and the reception was in the adjacent byres.

From the Mathers' window we watched Miss Jessie MacRae from Port at her lobster creels. A part-time worker at that time at Gallanach farmhouse, she had been on the island twenty-nine years and had been using her creels for a decade.

Lawrence MacEwen at that time was toying with the idea of establishing new crofts for "the right type of people." He hoped to find incomers, each with a specialist job who could help build up the community life on the island and make it self sufficient, sharing machinery and making money part-time on the farm.

I do not know if the plan has succeeded. I hope some day to return there—without a timepiece. Sitting in the young Mathers' cosy home on a sizzling wet day I realised my watch had stopped so I asked Bruce the correct time. "Tuesday," he replied. That is how it should be.

While on Mull I discovered another example of the practical but unhurried approach when in the Ross of Mull at Ardfenaig I came across a traditional 'neighbouring' clipping with several of the area's sheepmen gathered beside the old stone fanks helping with each other's stock. Near-neighbours Archie McCallum and John MacCormick had 300 and 350 ewes respectively and they and their helpers kept the old hand-shear tradition going, fortified by meals, which their womenfolk heated over the peat fire.

On the same day I went to Knock farm further over the island where Agricultural Training Board shearing instructor Donnie MacDougall was teaching the youngsters rapid machine clipping based on the methods perfected and made world-famous by that crack New Zealand shearman

87

Godfrey Bowen. The Bowen method is used in every pastoral country in the world.

Yet some of these old timers down at the Ardfenaig fanks told me that the moves and methods used today in the Bowen system are the same as those carried out by the hand-shearers in the long-gone past.

So folk are always learning. George MacDonald, the only full-time shepherd on the island of Coll when I was there in 1976, had much the same opinion. Beside the sheep pads and past many lochans between rock-strewn grazings he told me at the age of sixty-six: "As far as shepherding is concerned, you are learning all the days of your life. I know I am still going strong and still learning."

For the previous eighteen years he had tended a sizeable Blackface stocking between hefty sea breakers on either side of the island at Gallanach beside the lochs of na Cloiche, a' mhill 'Aird and nan Geadh.

In his younger days he could recall farms having three or four pair of Clydesdale horses each and he himself enjoyed working behind them. "When the horse era came to an end, the land went back," he told me.

Somebody doing a fair deal to improve his land was Kenneth Stewart whose farming enterprise over four farms, was the reason for my halt on the island. He was at that time moving back to what was once a traditional system, switching his emphasis from the big suckled calf seasonal trade to cheap overwintering, producing saleable store cattle at a later stage so that he could ship 180 head a year from the Inner Hebrides island.

Islands are warm hearted abodes. They also have the unexpected lying in wait. I had arrived on the isle following an all-night winter-time drive after speaking to a Young Farmers Club in the south of Wigtownshire. Leaving that airt at around 10 p.m. at night I just managed to reach the Oban ferry at 5 a.m. and after a nod at the island's hotel beside Arinagour, borrowed a hotel bike to visit Mr Stewart.

That night, he volunteered to drive me back in the Land Rover over the miles of spindly road to the hotel. Nonsense, says I, I have the bike. I said my farewells at an hour long after the darkening, jumped on my bike, discovered the lights were non-existent, tried to take a corner and it just was not there.

They either moved it, straightened it, stole it or had turned it the other way. So Biddy the bike and I parted company very suddenly, which immediately created a problem. How, with mud to the knees on a blashy winter's night in the middle of Coll, with the sky as black as jet, do you find a bike that has bolted.

In the second's semi-silence while the gale refreshed herself, Biddy's wheels could be heard still spinning several yards away. Had the wheels not sung out their hiding place in the night. I would have stepped into a 24ft deep sheuch (well, at least three feet deep) and a high-flowing burn.

So, one reckons, as he shamefacedly cadges a Land Rover lift back to base over the isle's ribboned road, that there is maybe as much safety and sanity on the motorways after all, than pedalling about the Inner Isles minus lights. And so much for saving £21 by not taking the car.

Mind you, even in daylight there was a stushie when Biddy—she was an excellent starter even on frosty mornings after being left outside behind Alastair Oliphant's warm and cheery hotel—got her head coming over the moorland by the Tireeman's Moss.

She mighty near gliffed a blackie whose glegness happily surpassed her innocence. It was good-looking grazing on that green strip in the middle of the road.

The best thing after a cowp, of course, it to get back on, so Biddy and I bounced off again next day to the island's north end on another assignment. Up the brae from Arinagour village, the gamekeeper came along in a Land Rover as a solid sheet shower came down, so Biddy was helped in the back beside the Labrador. Propped up in the back pointed at the back of my neck was a shotgun.

Boswell and Johnston came this road, they say. Whether they passed the burial ground of Cill Ionaig in the dark and wild and on a bike is not recorded. If they did, it is guaranteed they, too, would be mighty quick belting back down the Windy Gap, the isle's steepest mile by the looks of it. A soul is inclined to do these things if passing a lonesome cemetery in the dark and to blazes with pencils, notebooks, camera, films, etc. flying from the pockets.

Two innocent islanders returning in their motors probably saw the apparition and had to take evading action from a puffing pedlar who had not time to get off the road between Arinahost and Achamore.

Dammit, did Tam o' Shanter not do much the same? Even Jek Ri'path, the greatest yarnster of ferreting tales there is, did the same when, he says, "spacemen" with a blue light flashing—they had checked bonnets too—pursued him one night.

Medicinal recuperation was courtesy of Messrs. Bell, Dewars and Langs that night.

I did not need a bike on the next island—Kerrera—when I met in with Roy (Ned) Rimmer who faces the after-dawn hours atop the waves on Argyll's coastal waters, for his homestead was only a steep clutter of yards above the pier.

Ned and his collies were accustomed to the high morning air of sheepruns in Perthshire and Sutherland, but life in these 1977 days meant an early scud to Oban by dinghy or launch to collect newspapers and post, with a call at two or three slipways back down the side of the island to hand over the day's news. He also made a call at a tiny three-acre isle to look at his 'away-wintered' Blackface hoggs before plying back to the jetty at the foot of his croft to ferry folks across for their work in Oban.

Cheery Ned and his wife Margaret had put in their first year on Kerrera where he had taken over as ferryman and a few other things as well as having his twenty-acre croft. He had left a farm manager's job near

Lairg to take on the Kerrera post, based at a jetty which once saw many of the west island cattle near the start of their drove to the Falkirk Tryst.

There are tales of 1,800 cattle a year coming over from Mull to either Barr-nam-boc Bay or Port Dubh on Kerrera and then going—either across the Sound by vessel or being swum at the top end—to the mainland. Fees at one time were 8d for a cow between October and June or 10d for a fat beast in the back-end.

In the old days part of the drovers' compulsory payment to the ferryman was a bottle of whisky. This was not mentioned when I had, a year earlier, seen the Kerrera job last advertised or Ned might have found more competition from various quarters.

So, from 'herdings where perhaps company was sometimes thin on the ground, the Rimmers saw as many as 300 folks a day at the peak of holiday time. It provided continuous work for Ned who had a 15 ft dinghy with a 5 hp outboard and a 25 ft launch. He had also recently acquired a 28 ft landing craft on which he could tow livestock from the isle's farmers—and even a tractor and trailer—to the mainland.

While he was busy with the boats or his sheep—some were kept on the miniscule Heather Island—or popping round the isle on his motorbike with the newspapers and post, Margaret got on with making eatables for the tourists.

At that time she could cater for some eighteen visitors at her tea-room and on a good day the overflow would sit in the garden. She had to break off from her baking during my call to plank the herring creels on the back of the Shetland gelding, Coich, to haul up the school meals when Ned brought them across from the mainland to the jetty.

Folk and animals fairly make an island.

JEK'S 'HIGHLAND' JAUNT

The Royal Highland Show at Ingliston, Edinburgh is one of the most important events in the Scottish farming calendar. It brings together farmers and stockspeople from all over the UK and overseas. Here are some glimpses of the goings-on at the 'Highland' as seen through the eyes of a shepherd with whom I became well acquainted.

The 'Highland' lasts a day spun out to a year for the hillman. Burnhead folk, wisest of thinkers, toughest of critics, keenest of congratulators, yarn for a twelve-month on Ingliston's multifarious fare.

No, that's wrong. Many may rightly say multifarious, but for the outbye man who daily strides bent, over peat-hag and high sheep pads there are the three facets—and three only—on which he will regale from this June to next June those whose ears are receptive on the heights, at mart pens or in watering places.

Hill sheep. That is a certainty. Blackface and South Country Cheviot only though. Working sheepdogs—that's the next. (But there are no collies at the Highland—yes, yes, I know). And crooks. That's the third. The kind mind you, claimed from ram, hazel and elbow grease, fashioned for a role which so far has found no rival—worthwhile rival that is—on factory bench.

Dammit, but there are combines, corn-drills, muck-spreaders, cattle, MLC, DOAS, Colleges, steakbars, pigs, ponies, poultry, tools, fertilisers, breed societies, Boards for this and that, hoists, feeding stuffs, souvenirs, books, vaccines, barrows, lawnmowers, women, cutlery, clothes, facts, figures and lies?

Irrelevant, the lot. Sorry about that, Highland Show organisers. But the backaboot man is there for only three items—hill sheep, sheepdogs and sticks. According to Jek Ri'path anyway, and there is no better sage in shepherdom.

Backed by a wealth of travelling—he moved from a glenhead abode in Peeblesshire to kindlier hefts in Selkirkshire—and most noted now of the county's visionaries, ferreters, dykers, stonewatchers and stick-talkers, he seeks only at our mighty farming showpiece for furtherance of knowledge and information to fuse with inborn initiative. The fusion is disseminated through his shepherding skills and tasks. Without his like where would our uplands be?

It is said Jek Ri'path was the originator of that noted landsman's advice to the apprenticing young: "Keep your eyes open and your mouth shut."

Words though, are part of Jek's trade, second only to his everyday tasks. There were listeners aplenty one night as he relaxed from unloading a fellow shepherd's sheep followed by a walk round the bustling site on the evening before it opened to the public. (He said he had been unloading somebody else's sheep and brought the long coated, bold, lean collie Cleg to prove it, but there are a lot of folk who make excuses for getting into the Highland on the Sunday for a free look round. In Jek's case, at the sheep and sticks).

His listeners awaited the profound philosophies on what Ingliston offered. In the way of Blackfaces for instance. For two or three hours the show's most critical ringside will agree, disagree, accept, reject, concur and differ as the judge nobly makes his placings on the day of adjudication.

A judge of sheep and sheepdog trials—and I come into the latter category myself—is a man who cheerily starts the tasks with parents, relatives, friends, opinions, a Christian name, sanity, pride and profound knowledge and finishes the job bereft of the lot and the inability—rather inadvisability—to enter certain establishments within five years or sixty miles of the judging chore.

Jek's summing up of the penned Blackfaces did not take long. He had only looked at the rams anyway before he went to change his breath at the hostelry so handily placed next to the premier sheep ring.

"The breed's ruined," he announced to cronies who were established for the week in their showground billets. "Feenished, yeesless. There's no yin horn among that clutter-up o' tuips that wid make a lambin' stick. No' yin. They've het them, twusted them, poo'ed them, rived them, shoved them, yerked them and shapit them like fancy ornaments—fu' o' holes and burned bluid when ye come tae rasp a crook frae them. That'll dae Cleg! The man'll no hairm ye when he's streekit oot on the flair."

There was one notable shearling tup on show though, counselled a herding friend. "Aye, a' did hear tell o' yin," responds Jek. "But a' widnae louse him on ma' hill—hae'd never hie up oor burnheid, They've tae hae the e'e o' the de'il—no' a stamack fu' o' cabbage fur oor grun."

"Jeest like aul' Scuffler," added Jek rounding to his favourite subject. The said Scuffler, a lengthy, wise half-beardie is among Jek Ri'path's legendary pack of calibre collies, as worthy as any found on Scotland's uplands.

There have been other opposing descriptions of their worth, gait, temperament and looks sometimes—that includes Jek—when he has hied to the hill, but I can vouch that his beasts will do an honest day's work if given a week and a half, flaked maize and the odd braxy.

"Clever dug yon Scuffler," he continued. "Brains galore—hae'd even crawl ablow a barra' tae paint it. A' can set the alarm ootside his box tae gaun off at three o'clock on a clippin' mornin' and when a' stir aboot six o'clock hae hes half the six score yowes buchted—and that's wi' bringin' them doon yin at a time. Frae as far as six miles back. Wi' three rivers tae cross. Efter draftin' oot a wheen o' the neebor's stravaigin' sheep.' Here Cleg, dod deveritt, take that back tae the poultry shed."

The Cheviot men came in. "Some graun' pens ye hae there lads," says Jek whose knowledge of the great breed is as sincere and knowing as the reputation of his masterly dogs—home ground collies like the blue-grey barker Lunky, litter-mates Stook and Pook, the veteran mottle-nosed Birler, the reliable smooth-coated Grup and the bold Postie whose name and missing tail were due to over-exuberance on the long loaning to Jek's abode alongside a small red van belonging to E 11 R.

"A' can tell ye in a word whit a guid Cheviot should look like," said Jek without prompting. "In word. It's like this—say ye' had a richt stotter o' a day at the lambin'. Rain, and sleet blinin' doon, a dizzen cowpies, fower lambs drooned in the burn, seeven kebs, three gimmers no' sookin' their lambs, a gran' aul' reliable breeder gurried wi' a fox, the postman gettin' y'r ham and eggs and a wheen ither things.

"Ye fa' ben the hoose aboot ten o'clock at nicht and the aul' wumman says 'dy'ye fancy a half o' whusky?' Ye say aye. And she thins it doon immensely wi' anither whusky. Ye tak yin moothfae—noo . . . . yon's the expression a guid Cheviot should hae. Where ir ye Cleg, here come tae heel, so ye've fun' the steakbar hae ye, ye shilpit fag-'en."

Herds respect a talker. One with nature's gift of sense and logic. So they kept quiet awaiting the next verbal pronouncement. But there are dangers liking, comparing or contrasting Cheviot with Blackie in certain company. Rangers-Celtic stuff in a way and in the same fashion both do their stuff.

Cheviot that bit better though, according to Jek.

He is as easily upset with talk of internal combustion or machines that rely on that mode of operation. Says that these and Sitka Spruce are a scourge worse than a combination of scrapie, sturdy and louping ill. So it was maybe a mistake for a crony to try and switch the crack from Cheviot, Blackie and collie to enquire about Jek's liking of the new sound-proofed, multi-horse-power tractor units espied amidst the machinery stands which can be seen from the hostelry if you swing from the joists with your crook. (Some do, some do).

"Listen," grits Jek whose vehicular days, apart from youthful jaunts with the gird, have been confined to haulage floats. "Tractors, Land Rovers, jeeps, bikes—they're a' the same. Where's the stockmanship in them. That's the bother wi' sae mony sheepman noo—they mooch aroon' the hill wi' thae Land Rovers. That's no herdin'. Dod deveritt m'neebor's dugs'll no lift a lug unless the Land Rovers backed up tae their kennel door and they're lifted on. They wur never muckle yees onywi', except fur eatin.'

"A guid stick'll get ye anywhere weel enough wi'oot gettin' y'rsel taigled on wheels. A stick's got authority, sense, strength, reliability, purpose, style and a mind. What Land Rover has that?"

"Yin that a' can min' o', " muttered a crony. "The yin that took ye hame frae y'r sister's waddin' in Selkirk a wheen years syne. A stick widnae hae been muckle yees tae ye yon nicht. Min' you, ye were huntin' fur it—they couldnae get the hotel closed for y'rsel keklin' on, saying ye must hae left y'r dug and stick in the kirk fur ye couldnae fin' them."

"There wis a guid excuse fur it—a man is no often pairted wi' his twae best freens," said Jek. "Mind you there's some whackers o' crooks across there at the show the day. Braw, yeesless yins an' a', some a' deckit oot wi' fancy carvings. Nae yees fur the hill yon.

"A bricht-skinned Cheviot, a wyce half-beardie wi' spunk and biff, and roon-heidit well-spread crooks—it's a' that a' man needs. Which reminds me a'll hae tae be gettin' nearer hame. Cleg, d'ye hear—demmit hae's been wheengin' aboot again among thae Jacobs sheep. Spit it oot Cleg."

To leave sticks for just a minute, however, I should point out that the sheen of stockmanship on Ingliston's noisy acreage does not happen overnight. Folks do not just go out after the football results on the Saturday night and reckon that the well-bagged Ayrshire ecstatically sliding her flea-passengered rump up and down the whin bush in the wrong field is the ideal one to powder and pamper into shape for the Highland Show week's big winnings.

Neither do the deep-thinking sheep men, seeking maggots on their high pads a fortnight prior to the event, spot a ewe of strong, keen horn which they think will gain the major crack in the show-yards hostelries. Mind you, that is where all the big decisions are made. Oh yes, the judges with weary conscientiousness plod their way through what is paraded in front of them in the white-railed squares and please two folk—themselves and the victors. But for genuine unbiased discrimination, practical deliberation, inbred wisdom and unadulterated character assassination, that howff, seven pints length from the Blackface ring, is the famed forum.

I have heard myself of a winter's night—and there are many of them in shepherdom, some coming twice a day—a fabled man of burnhead lore and learning regale a gathering with his clinical description of every Blackie and Cheviot at that year's 'Highland.'

Yet myself and the other 325 listeners who have a far better recollection of the whole event can easily recall his attuning himself to the 10 a.m. air that day with a fair feed of dew from Elgin's vales, at midday the same liquid's sunburn prevention properties had delayed his stay in that heat-resistant haven; by three o'clock he had progressed to hunting cowpies in the same abode; and by six he himself resembled one with his pie-filled collie asleep across his frame. Don't ask how the dog came into it.

Anyway, it just does not all happen overnight on a sudden whim. What you see at Ingliston displaying horn, fleece, udder, hoof, muscle and feathering before the genuine judges is the culmination of many months of work—sometimes years of precise planning and pacing, nurturing the exhibits until they reach their proud zenith.

It had been six years previously, for example, since Jek Ri'path first realised he had the material to enter. Even that year's distinguished visitor, the Queen Mother, knew all this—the hopes, for instance over the years as a spunky young ewe lamb might turn into a whammer of a matronly ewe with alertness of eye, two-sided catering, planked beautifully on four legs, clipped like a rug and firm of flesh. There is at all the shows stock of a fair age which will prove that maturity of animal linked to stockmanship (and maybe showmanship) of exhibitor is a fair old combination.

A case in point is . . . . . it is six years previously since who first realised he had the material?

Yes, yes, Jek Ri'path. As a girdle fits to a swee, Jek Ri'path is thirled to high sheep rakes. He was still holding court in the stockmans' great meeting abode. This is the place for news. The Press pavillion is—mostly —for non-Press, hangers on and those who will make the headlines with pronouncements about the future price of supermarket meat to the detriment of hard-working livestock exhibitors who, because of the pronouncements of big retail chains, exporters, industry chiefs etc., etc., find there is no space left in the papers for their proud achievements. (The organisers of the Highland Show should ban all press conferences on the days in which judging is taking place so that the stockspeople and breeders get due recognition for their long, ungrudging work—after all it was the breeders and their workers who got the Highland going with their entries, not those who spend five minutes in a plane jotting down a few headline catching phrases).

"That's a clinker ye hae there, Jek," pronounced a fellow Border herd eyeing the Ri'path contributions to this Royal occasion. "This yin here Dood? Aye, yeesfae, yeesfae. She'll likely hae a guid keek at it the morn. She's a guid kenner.

"Thae Royalty, ye see Dood, thae hae a richt e'e fur tradeeshun . . . . tradeeshun wi' quality. She'll nae doot hae a right keek at that yin the morn' Dood and shae'll likely jeest say tae hersel: 'There has been a fair wheen 'oors went into getting this crook wrocht up fur the show.'

"A'll tell ye this Dood, there hes been a guid wheen mair oors than whit gaed into makin' some o' her dochter's mugs a'll tell ye that. Oors? It wis years—six o' them tae be exact.

"A' can aye min' the mornin' yet. A' wis getherin' the grun' abin the Whupple burn. M' aul' dug Cloaker wis gaun like oil. Whit a dug he wis Dood. A' hae seen Cloaker hunt a dizzen mawkit yowes frae ablow yon Rowan Tree on the breist o' the Grains hirsel, weir them across the low en' o' the loch in the bailiff's boat, bowff them through the cundy tae the stells, gurry them intae the dipper, gie them a meenit's peace tae dry and hunt them back tae their hirsel the same wey, pick up his stick and get on

95

wi' the rest o' his work again. Cloaker yince 'herded a swarm o' bees frae the glen-mooth doon into the Yarrow.

"Onywi', that day a' wis in the lirk o' the heid-en' grun' and a' wis stoppit in m' tracks. A' wis stoppit in m' tracks, Dood. Yon scrachle o' a wee tuip we bocht at Lockerbie fower years afore, wis tented on a knoweheid, Dood, whit a sicht.

"It wis like . . . it wis like . . . . it wis like coming across a crock o' gold fu' tae the brim wi' Islay water, Dood. Ye couldnae see his bad hin' leg, the drap in his tail-heid, not the short rib, and a' jeest thocht tae masel—ye hae something there that'll make the Heelan' show, gin a wheen years auld Scrauchly.'

"Nae doot, Dood. She'll see that Hersel' the morn! She's seen mony a guid yin Hersel' and a've heard she hes twae or three braw yins at hame. A' hae been telt—unofeechally of course, Dood, unofeechally—that she'll be gettin' the chance of that yin the morn if she takes a likin' tae it.

"Ye see, Her and ma'sel hae some things in common. Fishin' fur instance. Shae'll plitter away in yon burns o' hers fur 'oors, Dood. Jeest like m'sel."

"Weel, that's yin thing that's truthfae onywi," nods Dood getting in a word. "Y'r baith guid at fishing. But she gauns aboot it in bricht daylicht and she disnae coorie roon the hoose-en' jeest afore the darkenin' tae see if a' the lums doon the glen are quait then hie doon tae the burn wi' a hiyfork."

"Jeest fur support, Dood, jeest fur support. If a' wisnae hingin' ontae the fork a' could be slippin' in the burn."

Dood got another word in. What had old Scrauchly the Lockerbie purchase to do with Jek's current thoughts. An hour later he knew, filled to the brainlid with the happenings and hopes of six years—for a stickmaker knows a good horn when he sees one and tends to take care of it, especially a Cheviot, for they have not been pampered as much as the Blackface whose renown is now low with crookmen.

Whatever Scrauchly lacked in physique and finesse he made up for in the quality of his horns, an impression enhanced after Jek had sawn them off a few years back and further emphasised when at last he got round last winter to the hard graft of heating, squeezing, shaping, rasping, filing, chiselling and polishing. All of which took many, many weeks to accomplish—and an hour or so to describe that morning to his fellow 'herds.

Yet no one could deny that the warm-handed crook of thistle and scroll and a beautifully balanced hazel shank herried from the Duke of ---------'s woodlands one night three years ago, was a cracker.

Which left only one question, and it had to be blurted out by Dood. "Ye hiv jeest the yin guid yin there though Jek—auld Scrauchly hud twae handlebars. The rest o' y'r entry is gey middlin' and a'm shair auld Scrauchly's ither horn's no among that lot."

New born lambs get off to a healthy start with warm Spring weather and a good feed. *(Photo: G. Wright)*

The start of a drove on the Isle of Skye. *(Photo: National Museum of Antiquities of Scotland)*

Bob Wilson, one of the last of the Border drovers photographed at Harden Mains, Jedburgh, the starting point for many a long trek. *(Photo: Scottish Farmer)*

John Dickson 'Hill Herd', in his traditional garb of balaclava and plaid. *(B.B.C. Copyright Photograph)*.

Stanhope, Tweedsmuir, once the home of John Dickson the shepherd poet. *(Photo: Scottish Farmer)*

At the end of another long gather at Cairndow, between Arrochar and Inveraray. *(Photo: Scottish Farmer)*

The shepherds of Cairndow enjoy a blether after a gather in 1968. *(Photo: Scottish Farmer)*

Getting steam up at a threshing at Over Howden, Lauder, in the early part of this century. *(Photo: National Museum of Antiquities of Scotland)*

Veteran millman Joe Coulthart is reunited with an old mill unit at the Royal Highland Show, Ingliston, Edinburgh, 1978. *(Photo: Scottish Farmer)*

CLAYTON & SHUTTLEWORTH'S
NEW CATALOGUE, No. 77,
WITH REVISED LIST OF PRICES OF
PORTABLE ENGINES & THRASHING MACHINES
WITH OR WITHOUT PATENT COMBINED GUARD AND FEEDER.

ACTION ENGINES, STRAW ELEVATORS and STACKERS, HORIZONTAL FIXED ENGINES, CIRCULAR SAWS, CORN MILLS, &c., &c.

CAN BE OBTAINED, POST FREE, BY APPLICATION TO
CLAYTON & SHUTTLEWORTH, LINCOLN.
LOMBARD STREET, LONDON; and 35 & 37 TARLETON ST., LIVERPOOL.

An early advert from *The North British Agriculturist*, March 1878. *(Photo: National Museum of Antiquities of Scotland)*

One of the shepherding and sheepdog world's genuine characters, John Murray, with his international trials champion, Glen. *(Photo: T. Phin)*

The Dumfries Fair, 1890. One of the busiest fairs in the South of Scotland. *(Photo: Ewart Library, Dumfries)*

A selection of crooks bearing game and fish designs made by Norman Tulip. *(Photo: Scottish Farmer)*

Sheepdog Trials champion Raymond MacPherson and some of his prizewinning dogs head for the hills. *(Photo: Scottish Farmer)*

Maybole bootmaker Dick Goudie, working at his ancient craft on machinery which is over a hundred years old. *(Photo: Scottish Farmer)*

Dick Goudie displays a pair of his own hand made boots. *(Photo: Scottish Farmer)*

The Maori man and his dog. Dubby Powers at the 1975 Expo' Trials at Rotorua, New Zealand. *(Photo: Matt Mundell)*

Raymond MacPherson on his way to winning the World Sheepdog Trials Championship in Delaware, U.S.A., 1973 *(Photo: J. Glenn Crawford)*

Competitors at the 1973 World Sheepdog Trials Championship receive their instructions from organiser John Shropshire. *(Photo: Matt Mundell)*

Margaret Rimmer collects school dinners for the children on the Island of Kerrera, Argyllshire. *(Photo: Scottish Farmer)*

The author takes a break at Barnhill near Dumfries during one of his expeditions into sheep country. *(Photo: Hugh Thompson)*

John Campbell's Nell, which helped to take the Scottish Sheepdog Trials brace Championship title north of Inverness for the first time. *(Photo: Scottish Farmer)*

John Murray's Glen, winner of the supreme International Sheepdog Trials Championship 1971. *(Photo: Scottish Farmer)*

Robert Shennan with Mirk, the supreme International Sheepdog Trials Champion 1978. *(Photo: Marc Henrie)*

Bobby Wood's Liz, a regular in the Scottish National Trials team and a former International Shepherd's champion. *(Photo: Scottish Farmer)*

George Hutton from Threlkeld, Cumbria, with Nap and Nip, two consistent Sheepdog Trials winners. *(Photo: Loftus Brown)*

Geoff Billingham, a Yetholm shepherd who spends his spare hours drawing country scenes. *(Photo: Scottish Farmer)*

Shepherd artist Geoff Billingham at his everyday work on the hill. *(Photo: Scottish Farmer)*

Joe Johnstone, a Dumfriesshire farmer with a multi-musical talent, plays his set of antique glasses. *(Photo: Scottish Farmer)*

A team of drystane dykers at work near Shawhead, Kirkcudbrightshire. *(Photo: Scottish Farmer)*

Marathon mountain runner Joss Naylor. *(Photo: Farmers Weekly)*

A big team at a sheep shearing, Mull 1919. *(Photo: National Museum of Antiquities of Scotland)*

Wiston Cap, the 1965 International Sheepdog Trials Champion.

John Gilchrist's Spot, twice Scottish National Trials Champion. *(Photo: Scottish Farmer)*

Thomson McKnight's Gael, the 1967 International Supreme Champion. *(Photo: Scottish Farmer)*

David Shennan's Maid, one of the most prolific Scottish Sheepdog Trials' prizewinners *(Photo: Matt Mundell)*

William Cormack's June, the 1973 Scottish Sheepdog Trials Champion. *(Photo: Scottish Farmer)*

John Richardson, one of Scotland's best known sheepdog handlers with Mirk, his 1975 National Champion.

Water diviner Edwin Taylor of County Durham with his whalebone dowsing rods. *(Photo: Matt Mundell)*

Dick Fortune of Edinburgh, who spent part of his life in New Zealand and is now a well known competitor at British sheepdog trials. *(Photo: Scottish Farmer)*

Andrew Renwick of Dalkeith, who could recall the days of city centre dairy herds in Edinburgh. *(Photo: Scottish Farmer)*

Donald MacLeod of Bonar Bridge, a past Scottish and International Sheepdog Trials Shepherds Champion. *(Photo: Scottish Farmer)*

John Angus MacLeod of Lairg, a much travelled sheepdog handler. *(Photo: Scottish Farmer)*

Mrs. Annie MacCormack of Kingussie, the first lady handler to take part in the International Sheepdog Trials. *(Photo: Scottish Farmer)*

Shepherd Robin Horne of Taynuilt and his kelpie sheepdog Corrie. *(Photo: Scottish Farmer)*

John Murdoch's two stumpy tailed sheepdogs. *(Photo: Scottish Farmer)*

Peter Hetherington's Hemp proves to be a bad loser at the Lockerbie International Sheepdog Trials 1976. *(Photo: Scottish Farmer)*

Brothers Alex and William Waugh from Sanquhar, following in the shepherding footsteps of their father and grandfather. *(Photo: Scottish Farmer)*

Peter Hetherington's Nell, a former Scottish Trials Champion and regular Internationalist. *(Photo: Scottish Farmer)*

John Thomas took the International Supreme Championship to Wales in 1977. *(Photo: Scottish Farmer)*

Gwyn Jones of Penmachno, North Wales won the International Supreme Championship in 1974 and 1976. *(Photo: Matt Mundell)*

Tom Watson of Lauder with Jen, the 1980 International Supreme Champion. *(Photo: Jack Fraser)*

Irish sheepdog handler Martin O'Neill and his International collie Risp. *(Photo: Scottish Farmer)*

It's hard work herding sheep. *(Photo: Scottish Farmer)*

"A'll be on m' wiy then lads," coughs Jek. "A'll jeest get thir sticks ower tae the tent for the judgin."

"The ither horn, Jek?" pursues Dood.

"So a'll miybe see ye later on then folks. A'm keen tae get some tickets on thir sticks, fur Hersel' tae see the morn, especially this yin' off the aul' tuip."

"The ither horn," quizzed Dood.

"Weel, let's pit it this wiy, Dood," said Jek, knowing there was no way out. "A lot of things can happen tae horns when y'r working on them. Ye can loss them, ye can crack them in the vice, ye can roast them ower hard ower the lamp, ye can rasp them too sair, ye can slip wi' a file or a chisel when y'r at an intricate pairt, or ye can split them when y'r drillin' a hole fur the shank. Ither things can happen as weel."

The reaction to all that was, "aye, go on."

"So a' wis gettin' on bonnily wi' this yin frae that ither horn, reckonin' it wid be a corker fur the show. A graun' sweep o' the heid wi' a braw roon' heel on it. And yin' o' m' best yet thistle and scrolls jeest about feenished. It wid hae been spoiled if it hed been ony better. A hed jeest a wee bit mair bane tae scrape oot wi' the wife's nail-file and it wis feenished tae perfection."

Jek made for the door. Again, the silence until Dood asked: "Well, whit happened. Did ye slip wi' the file, did it no' fit the shank, did it fa' and get crackit or did ye loss it or something?"

Retreat by Jek out of the door was accompanied by a mumbled; "No, aul' Cloaker got haud o' it aff the tap o' the dresser and scoffed it."

"Dogs are aye fond o' horn a'body kens that," said Dood after Jek had departed to the stick-making competition. "Be a tragedy fur him—terrible efter a' his plans fur that horn. And he aye ettled on showing Royalty whit a dab hand hae wis at the crooks."

"Onywi' miybe She'll be seein' auld Scrauchly's ither horn the morn if shae ca's by—ye never ken, there could be a championship ticket on it and Jek'll be back in here the next day kecklin' like a cockerel aboot his stick."

"Hae'll be back sinner than that," said Dood's companion. "The sticks were a' judged at the week-en—hae is ower late at getting them across."

So Jek went home. But he was back again the next year with new enthusiasm. The outbye man can breenge into Ingliston aglow later in the week's activities, his bonnet jaunty and his ears stirred by the chirruping song he has come to hear. One thing brings many of them back—the rhythm, magic, tang and weave of the shearers' skills as they tussle for the national title. There is landsman's ballet about the whirl and gliding artistry of the shearers' handpieces following the contours of the upended ewes.

Ninety-nine per cent of the glen dwellers who flock to see the woollen-breeked and black-vested men on the shearing board will admit they themselves have not the quality or the pace of those on the platform.

There is one per cent, however, who in his own words could "whup the 'oo aff twae hale hirsels o' ill-fed wethers wi' yin haun, on tap o' the kirk steeple, and wi' a sark-tail tied roon m' e'en while yon codgers wi' thur cleckin' machines are still tryin' tae fin' the place tae stert on thur first yin."

Jek Ri'path then, sheepman from bunnet to buits, felt that what would be seen on the shearing stances at Ingliston that week—and to me they are the country's topsters—were just the second best. A soul should make up his own mind about these things, but at the same time a man and his reputation bear a howffworth of listening.

For some, however, it could be painful. It was possible that day to see nearhand some of the sheep pens, a shepherd or two with new hairstyles, and in the drinks dispensary building next to the judging rings, the odd scud of bonnet-curled hair lying on the floor following the previous night's discussion on the attributes of the great Borders clipping man.

Jek is of the old clippers school, a dab hand with the hand-shears. A blade man, in our hill lingo. Or a tongs man. Few are left, and those who have stayed are relics of an era which is now a sepia-coloured one of a score of clippers, catchers, wool-rollers, soup-cooking wives, baggers, buist-covered herds' weans and oatmeal water and whisky crocks beside the dyke at glen shearings.

The trouble the previous night, as some of the 'herds recounted the next morning, was that Jek had taken along his shears to the annual general meeting of the Herdsman's Sunday night at the Highland Resident's Society. Worthwhile educationally but on recollection—I think—an unwise decision later on at night.

Shepherdom contains some who regularly in howff confabs hold the cat's beam-end to the sun. Dood Wid, a crony of Jek in that great lamb-rearing strath in Selkirkshire, is of such ilk, mainly because of his own prowess with the machine cutters and combs (300 hoggs in a day once) and also because he feels Jek with his Cheviots is in the wrong sheep breed. Without in any way being biased, he is totally wrong on the latter, mind you.

Jek was kindled instantly by Dood's dig about his non appearance in this year's entry for the shearing championship. "Hmph, fur yae thing thae dinnae hae enough sheep tae keep me gaun tae denner-tum, whut dae ye say eh, Cleg," chirps Jek. His long-coated bold and lean bowley-legged collie of character, pith and teeth, eyed him in praise.

A few onlookers sensed another day of yarns so true and flawless to be almost false and to Dood's jest about his friend being slower than a "kitten fle'en efter a ferret," Jek responded. "Did a' tell ye aboot the day a' wis jeest in the stell ma'sel and a' hed clippit a hirsel afore the cock crew. A' stoppit a while tae get dressed and when the wife yelled oot it wis denner-tum maun, a' wis gaun sae fast it taen me ten mair yowes tae slow ma'sel doon.

98

"A didnae even need tae raise ma'sel off m' stool. Yon great dog o' mine, Slurp, brocht every yowe tae ma sheet, cowpit them, dagged them, pit the buist mark on and hied them a' back tae their lambs when a' wis feenished."

"A' can min' o' seein' that Jek, richt enough," says Dood in the growing silence of interest and intrigue. "An' did aul' Slurp no keep bringin' ye back yins that still had hauf their wool left on. Ye made sic a bad job, some o' the yowes wur ashamed tae gaun back tae thur lambs. When ye turned them oot tae the hill, a' thocht it lookit like refugees frae a first aid practise cless wi' a' yon plaisters ye had put ower their cuts."

Jek eyed his other dog, the grey-nosed stumpy-tailed Birler who had taken on the role of chief pint-glass cleaner, and that on top of the bar too. He saw a barful of ears awaiting an explanation. "There wid be the odd kickin' aul bissom deservin' o' a bit nip tae lairn her a lesson. Thae fowk wi' their fancy gear wull fin' it'll be the same the morn, Dood."

"Kickers, Jek! A' heard tell ye swore sae much that yin aul' yowe keeled ower an' expired at the noise—and she wis hauf a mile away at that. A hae heard tell ye c'n gaun through the sheep as fast as a cobalt bullet but there hes tae be workmanship. Ye ken, like some o' thae New Zealand lads that come ower tae show us."

The silence got louder. New Zealand clipping is world famous of course. It is the land of the deucer (200 a day shearers), the drummer (the slowest), the fleece-o (he fills the catching pens with sheep), the smoko (tea-break), the tar-boy (he puts tar on cuts made by the shearers) and the basher (a rough shearer). And of legendaries whom I've spellbindingly watched with Maori musterers and back country sheep tenders near Rotorua.

But New Zealand, too, is a word combination one should not use near Jek Ri'path. "Thir tongs here," says Jek unveiling his shears in front of the gallery "and the maun that's ahint them could show ony o' they big-heidit beer-slurpin' Kiwi laggers, mair style 'n speed 'n workmanship on drookit, wild wethers in a blizzard an' oor efter a'd come hame frae a herds supper than they'd lairn in a twal-month frae ony fancy instruction book.

"Show me a man here the morn that could doff twa hunner and twuntyeicht Cheviots in a day wi' the tongs and dae the catchin' and rowin' himsel'. Eh? A' hae polished off a hunner munyatime afore the wife brocht oot the ten o'clock scones."

"A hundred whuskies is that eh, Jek" queried Dood stirringly to background chuckles newly taken over from disbelief at Jek's 228-a-day claims with his blades. "A' heard tell ye cut doon on the drinken' when ye stert the clippin' and ye jeest stick tae doobles till it's a' past. Onywi' ye hivnae telt onybudy hoo lang it taen ye tae shave yon Jacobs tuip belanging' tae the boss's wife. Ye huvnae managed tae tell onybudy hoo ye hung on tae a' fower horns thegither as ye gaed sailin' doon the loanin'

99

and crashed intae the Post Office van scraiching something aboot it's time a' goats were banned frae the country."

Jek's blades clicked nervously and threateningly away in the air as he surveyed Dood's glee and the 'what's going to happen' attitude of the watchers. Cleg sunk lower into the floor. A collie can detect a riled master long before he himself knows he's riled as we who watch sheepdog trials know. Unfortunately a dog's awareness of this sometimes leaves him what appears to be a smile on his face.

What happened after that is perhaps best not recalled. You would, as I have said, see the odd 'herd with an ultra-short haircut at that particular Highland Show. And the former long-coated Cleg was feeling a bit draughty too.

THE BLUE RIBAND

The International Sheep Dog Trials are now one of the country's biggest drawing pastoral events. Handlers from the four home nations who have gained team places in their own countries, attempt over three hard days to gain one of the major prizes in agriculture, the Supreme Championship.

"It was a red letter day for the knights of the plaid, and this they seemed to fully realise. Many grey-bearded veterans were there, some to try their skill, and others to look upon the prowess of their brethren. There was no envy or jealousy evinced, each new arrival being received in the most cordial manner. When the great masters of the sheepdog world made their appearance there could be seen in the faces of the younger and less tried men a look of pride that their profession could boast such heroes."

So *The Scottish Farmer* reported the first-ever International Sheep Dog Trials in their issue of 30 August 1906. The trials were held at Gullane Hill, East Lothian with twenty-seven entries. First prize went to Robert Sandilands, Dundas Castle with Don.

Today the International Trials—held alternatively in Scotland, Wales and England—annually draw thousands of people from home and, increasingly, overseas. For many from the pastoral areas, it is the choice for an annual holiday.

From that original event where twenty-seven entries were taken, the International now comprises teams of fifteen from Scotland, Wales and England and eight from Ireland (including the Isle of Man) to give a total of fifty-three handlers trying to qualify for the fifteen-dog supreme championship regarded as the Blue Riband of the sheepdog world. In addition there are the doubles classes and driving contest.

The teams consist of the top-pointed collies from each country's own National event and these can draw entries exceeding 200 dogs. In 1981 there were 180 runs in the singles competition at the Scottish National, just under 200 at the Welsh National, 230 at the English and 80 at the Irish. One could say then that the victor was the best of 690 dogs which had set out to try and claim the big award.

I have already chronicled elsewhere in these pages the deeds of some International champions—Raymond MacPherson, John Murray and Thomson McKnight—and will look now briefly at some of the others whom I wrote about in the last decade and a half.

There have been several Welshmen victorious in that time and I can vividly recall in 1968 when we left them still singing under the shadow of towering Cader Idris mountain and plying their tributes on the homeliest of sheepdog men. Llyr Evans. He had left these valleys thirty years previously and come back to his birthplace that year—as a member of the English team for a handler runs at National level in the country of his residence—to win the supreme honour.

Around places like Tyrau Mau, Mynydd-y-Gaden, Pen-y-Gaden and Llyn-l-Cau, Llyr in his early days instilled into himself and his dogs the kind of quiet confidence we saw that day in 1968 when he won the supreme over the flat course at Towyn. "If you can go to the post with confidence you are there," Llyr told me. "If you get these dogs to do things for you at home and their temperament is right they will do things away from home."

It is the attitude of a handler who, when you see him sometimes on a trials course or at home in a pleasant part of the English countryside, leaves the impression he is liable to take a cup of tea with him to the trials post.

When I visited him at Whittlebury, near Towcester, he admitted life had been hard to begin with. They stirred early in his home valleys. By 3 a.m. sometimes the collies would be on high Cader Idris hunting off the mountain sheep from the ferns for the clippings. It was worth maybe five shillings a day to some. Thirty shillings for a long tiresome week was the reward for a keen young sheep worker.

In those days the valleys around the mountain, looking across to Cardigan Bay in Merionethshire saw many able youngsters with their dogs, half-bred Border Collies with bark and force.

"At one time I would help to gather and clip practically all these valleys, right up to Cader Idris," said Llyr. "It was all open mountain then, not as you see them today with the grass fields and the cropping to near the top. We could take three or four hours to gather from these tops."

All Llyr's relations were on hill farms so there were always good dogs. "Mind you there were not nearly so many trials that we could reach. We had to travel by train and then maybe walk a few miles. It could be quite costly for a youngster."

Expensive or not, there seems to have been a good many top men from that area. Black and white Jess, a bitch belonging to his brother John, was the first collie Llyr ran around 1922. Off Hunter's Sweep and Tom Dickson's Fly, she had quite a few prizes to her credit.

Llyr's move to Leicestershire severed a lot of his old Welsh connections but these were all rekindled in 1968 when he took to Towyn his stylish Bosworth Coon, a rough-coated collie which was then five years old. Coon was by his own Bosworth Scot and Fly dogs. Fly was a granddaughter of Millar's Speed while Scot was the International driving champion of 1962. There was a wealth of Scottish and Welsh blood in Coon right back to former Welsh and International champion, Hughes' Jaff and also Wilson's Cap. Through Scot, Coon also went back to Bobby

MacKay's Ben from Wooler (son of Whitehope Nap and MacKay's Tibbie) and David Dickson's Lass. And through Fly he had the blood of Ted Jones' Drymen-bred Haig and R. J. Davies' Fly.

Coon looked promising at about five months old. He was about eight months old when Llyr developed blood poisoning. So Coon was sent to Gwyn Jones of Penmachno—we will come across him in a few pages—who gets the credit for the initial breaking and training. It was under the commands of this North Wales handler that Coon won his first trial from about eighty collies at fifteen months old. Llyr took him home that back-end to add the final polish which was to earn him a mammoth collection of awards even before the Towyn International.

The year after Bosworth Coon took the supreme, he nearly completed a double at Chester. At the end he finished as runner-up. This international turned up another worthy at the head of the prize handout—the highly respected and experienced Harry Huddleston with his bitch Bett from Snab Green farm on the side of the Lune Valley in Lancashire.

I yarned later at his fireside with Harry and learned that his bitch had been unwanted. "Throw her in the back of Harry's Land Rover" said one of a trio discussing her in the nearby village of St Michaels. The young Bett was shoved inside the rear of the vehicle. A few days later she ran away from her new home and was lost for a week.

But she returned to work mainly on pedigree Friesians, a Dalesbred sheep flock "when necessary" and to return to Lancashire the coveted supreme championship prize. These dales had contributed many kindly chapters in collie history, although up to that time the supreme had only gone twice to that county.

Bett was the second to earn it. But who was to know that when she was pushed into Harry's Land Rover? Yet is was not entirely a surprise for two facts played a big part in her destiny. For one thing the owner was now Harry Huddleston, a man at the top of the trade as a trainer and a handler. And the other was Bett's ancestry. Although then unregistered, she went back through Lancashire blood to a blue bitch renowned in the north with Harry's father. So the two attributes fused.

Lune Valley is the airt for Huddlestons and Longtons. Both families have brought many honours to the region—including Tim Longton's winning of the supreme the previous time the International was at Chester—and in both cases a lot of success stemmed from the blood of that blue bitch Nell.

"My father had her at trials before 1914 and she had forty-five prizes out of fifty trials," Harry told me. He added that Bett was one of the easiest dogs he ever had to break "but she is learning yet. Everyday work does her. She does not have any extra training though she might be better if she did."

There was plenty of championship blood in Bett's history. For one thing she was a grand-daughter of Joe Gorst's Bet, a former English national and driving champion and the 1953 International driving champion. And grandsire, Ernest Holliday's Roy comes from the strain of Wallace's Moss, Scott's Kep, Armstrongs Don, Baty's Hemp, Telfer's Haig, Brown's Spot, Roberts' Jaff and Wilson's Craig. It was pretty certain too that Bett's mother took in J. M. Wilson's Cap at least half a dozen times in her pedigree and also the same maestro's Roy, three times winner of the International supreme.

The following year—1970—saw the supreme award return to Scotland when David McTeir stepped forward at Kilmartin, near Lochgilphead to receive the accolades after his partnership with the black, white and tan rough-coated Wiston Bill. David was by then shepherding at Cademuir, near Peebles, and two years earlier when I was there he was still helped by Mirk, the collie which won him the International Shepherd's championship of 1964.

A smallish dog, Mirk had been a noted breeder of hill collies and he was eight and a half the year he won the 'Herds title to be followed by runners-up placing for the supreme. Amends were made at the 1970 event with Wiston Bill, Mirk's son. Walter Hetherington bred Bill's mother Fly, also the dam of the 1965 supreme Wiston Cap. Fly goes back through Wilson's Bill 11 and Jack Hogarth's Lassie and includes Wilson's old Bill, Nap and Moss.

At that time Wiston Bill was accompanied in his Peeblesshire herding of some 600 Blackface ewes by Vic, which won the Shepherds International championship in 1967 at Stirling.

David McTeir, though now off 'herding duties, is rarely without a top dog for trialling or breeding and to the fore in 1972 came his half white-faced Ben which won both the Scottish and International Shepherds' championships and became a noted breeder. He was a Wiston Cap son out of Russell's Bess whose parents, Russell's Tess and J. Simpson's Jim were unregistered but go away back to Wattie Little's Spot, Wilson's Nap, Moss, Mirk and Cap, Purdie's Tam, Kirk's Nell and Hislop's Glen among others.

David McTeir's victory was the beginning of a three-year run of Scottish triumphs at the top followed by John Murray at Cardiff in 1971 and then John Templeton at Newcastle in 1972. We badly needed the latter that year for his work salvaged the supreme championship from plummeting into the most abysmal session it had been for a long time.

It had been a dismal day until mid-afternoon when John, crook below his oxter and poised atop the bales, watched with confidence the black and white Cap gather his first half score of ewes and start a drove which brought blessed relief and re-assurance.

John had started the trip to that grand victory when he was a twelve year old at his local Sorn trial in the late 1940's hunting out a little bitch Moss which he got for nothing from an uncle, and which was later to breed his much respected Roy, the first sheepdog I ever wrote about after watching him work at Blackriggs farm, Mauchline, following his 1957 Scottish National victory.

But 1972 pushed that into the background with the 4½ year old Cap, another son of Wiston Cap. On hand that Saturday night to receive the trophy for breeding the new champ was Strathkinness shepherd, the late Sam Carr who many a time ran Cap's dam, Moira, a daughter of Corbett's Roy and Aitken's Meg, the latter going back to Davie Dickson's Ben.

When I visited John that winter at his dairy and sheep farm of Airtnoch, Fenwick, he told me: "The work at home is done better with a dog that is trained for trials work. It is a great benefit at home—and of course that is the object of trials.

"When I start with dogs I train them for the big job (the International supreme with its two separate gathers of sheep half a mile distant) right away, and if they do not show any promise I do not go any further with them. But there are a lot of things which can go wrong even if they are fit to do it."

John says he picked up his sheepdog knowledge as he went along. "I tried to rectify my own mistakes, and it was a case of trying to learn the finer points. They were gey rough when I started. I am far better equipped now for training dogs, for there is a big expanse of hill here.

"There is a great satisfaction in winning an International—but there is also something taken away," said John. "There is nothing left to strive for. The International championship is what we all aim for all the time. Now I have gained it, I feel there is not much more I can do with the dog—except try and win it again."

Since then John nearly achieved the new ambition. He was runner-up at Stranraer in 1979 and third at Bala in 1980, but not with the same Cap. I last saw him in that 1973 'World' championship in America and soon after that he was sold to Fred Bahnson.

After the Newcastle International the Welshmen got a grip on the supreme award for a couple of years. When the trials re-visited Bala in 1973 to celebrate the centenary of such pastoral events which had begun there, Glyn Jones a part-time market yardsman from a smallholding perched on the hill by Bodfari gained the title everybody wanted that particular year.

"You must have luck to go to the International and luck to go through to the final," said Glyn when I called at his farm where he had Friesian milkers and cross Cheviot sheep. "But it isn't all luck. You must be prepared for it beforehand."

So he thought seriously when Bob Jones of Denbigh told him at his work one day, "Glyn, I have a good one for you."

The 'good one' was Gel, one of the most strikingly marked dogs of recent years to win the supreme. "He was very easy to break. I don't think we have actually fallen out, him and I," said Glyn.

Gel had some of his preparatory work on the common grazing

mountain behind Glyn's homestead. The 800-acre hump of a mountain sorts out a lot of young dogs which Glyn breaks, for in a way, training was another of his professions as well as farming and his droving duties at marts in Denbigh, Ruthin and St. Asaph.

One of the first lessons he instils is to get the dogs to lie down and 'come here.' His father trained his collies indoors. He had them going round the room from corner to corner learning their commands. "I used to do it too and may still do so with the odd ones in the winter," said Glyn. "They will take up commands quicker indoors. I do all the practical work on the mountain and add any polishing down here because you must be nearhand to get the polish."

Through his sire, Elwyn Griffith's Craig, a Gilchrist's Spot son, Gel had the blood of Bathgate's Rock, Hardie's Hope, Wilson's Moss, Hetherington's Anne and Cockburn's Mist. And on the maternal side, his dam, W. T. Williams' Nell has the strain of Watson's Shep, Holmes Bros' Lad, Dickson's Ben, Walker's Craig and Kirk's Nell.

It was a Jones on top again the next year—1974—when the trials returned to Kilmartin in Argyllshire. This time Gwyn Jones who lives at quiet Penmachno cushioned below the forest and the slate caverns among farmers, power station workers, pipeline men and shopkeepers and handling his black and white Bill, a Scottish-bred dog which went through several hands before he went to Wales.

Strangely enough it was at the previous Kilmartin International when he was sitting in the grandstand that Gwyn heard about the medium-coated Bill.

Few abodes could have such a glint of silver as his home at Cae Llwyd when I was there in the winter of 1974. About forty trophies crowded the living room in front of the traditional Welsh grate and twenty-seven of these had been won outright. A mighty collection for one of the youngest-ever International supreme champions. Gwyn's family had 220 ewes and 50 hoggs on the mountain with grazing in the fields shared with Friesian cows and followers. Gwyn's work included retailing the farm's bottled milk down in Penmachno in the mornings, except for the occasional time when a longish trip to a trial meant he perched the bottles on the doorsteps late the previous night.

His trial dogs, however, never worked with the milking cows. "I do not believe in having them among the cattle. I think they are too valuable for that and many dogs have been killed at that kind of work. But I certainly believe in shepherding work for them and they have to be good on the mountain here, for it is unfenced. When the sheep are on the mountains the dogs are up there nearly every day. It is not an easy mountain and it can be necessary sometimes to move a thousand sheep. What makes it worse is that there are high rashes, and in hot weather it takes a lot out of the dogs."

As we have seen earlier in this chapter it was also this ground where

Bosworth Coon got some of his early tuition.

The way to Cae Llwyd for the 1974 supreme, Bill, was a bit different. A son of Wiston Cap and W. Kinstrey's Nan from Greenlaw in Berwickshire, Bill had been in a few Scottish and Welsh hands by the time of the 1970 Kilmartin International which saw Gwyn sitting in the grandstand next to D. R. Owen of Llanllechid, near Bangor. They were both watching John Richardson's grand Mirk — the qualifying round champion at the event — and the Bangor man told Gwyn he had a half-brother. "The sheep were bad at that time too and I asked him if the dog would be able to manage these sheep," said Gwyn. He was told 'yes' and a fortnight after Kilmartin, Gwyn bought Bill from Mr Owen.

His acquisition, then two years old, had paternal blood back through Cap to J. M. Wilson's Bill 11 and Nap and on the maternal line took in the power of David Murray's Vic and Number, Dickson's Ben and John Gilchrist's old Spot.

"He took about three months before he would really come to work, but as soon as I started working trials with him I knew he was going to make the grade," said Gwyn. Since then Bill went on to average about five trials victories a year.

The day I was in Gwyn's homely company I saw a young Cornish-bred collie, the black and white Shep at work in the fields. Dammit, the next time the International was held in Scotland — at Lockerbie in 1976 — Gwyn gained his second supreme with the Shep dog. And he must have been a very disappointed man in 1978 at that classic Chatsworth International when he did not get the top rung again. He will be back for the hat-trick one of these days.

There was another Welsh visitor in the 70's — John Thomas. In 1977 he and his countrymen were far far better dogged than the other countries and so at Sennybridge were the masters of one of the mightiest tasks ever faced at the International trials.

The Welsh that year not only beat us, they truly clobbered us on ground under the shadows of the sharp-headed Brecon Beacons with practical management of long-tailed Brecknock Cheviots over the most talked about and certainly the most challenging course for many a day.

We had to face it — they had at that time that little bit extra magic down there. The course was the kind a lot of us had been clamouring for for many years, a daunting natural hectareage of hillocks and hollows which frightened the bonnets off some of the visitors. A sorter-out of genuine dogs and poultices. It did just that too. Nothing but good can come from these kind of tests.

John Thomas had shepherded this ground until two years previously. But since we had first set keekers on the black and white rough-coated Craig at the Bala Centenary event in 1973 and again in 1976 when he won the Qualifying and Shepherds' awards at Lockerbie he was among the obvious favourites for the supreme anywhere. His victory at Sennybridge came when he was around 7½ years old.

The white-vested Craig came as a nine-month-old pup to John. "He was as tough as hell to break," said John when photographer Niall Robertson and I visited him during a blinding snowstorm two months after his victory. He was then a thousand feet above the valleys of South Wales between Llandovery and Sennybridge but later moved to new pastures further west.

"I never had such a willing dog," said John. "I have seen me go to gather at five or six in the morning and when I got back at 12 o'clock he was still running. And in the afternoon he never refuses to work. He is a quick dog to catch on to what you want him to do, but hell of a fast. He is there before you have a chance to stop him. If you do not have him out every day he will lead you a dance."

A son of Leslie Suter's former International Chip which goes back through D. L. Evans' Bill and R. H. Williams' Meg to Herbert Worthington's Moss, Holmes' Ben, Millar's Lad and Harry Greenslade's Glen, Craig is out of Harold Hawkens' blue mottled bitch Jill. She is a daughter of his home-bred Jess put to Andrew Chapman's former Scottish International Garry which was by Jim Walker's Cap and J. Kirk's Nell.

"He is a consistent dog—he is not up today and down tomorrow," said John. "He puts on a fair show all the time. He can do anything. He has not a fault in him and he is a tremendous outrunning dog. He can be just a dot in the distance—he will maybe go out too far. Certainly he will go out a mile—no bother at all and you can turn him further back from that."

I can vouch for that for when we visited John's homestead we were barely able to see Craig at the horizon of his work and it was certainly well outwith the camera's range.

Old Craig even played football with the Thomas kiddies or visiting children and often, if in the house, would go to an upstairs window just to make sure he was not missing anything that was going on outside. And in the same frame of mind he insisted on taking the front passenger seat in John's car while Mrs Thomas had to be content with a back seat.

If we thought the Sennybridge course was a cracker, the next year was even tougher. On vast natural stockland steeped in history and walked by North-bred Masham and mule ewes, fallow deer, pheasants and milkers, Scottish farmer Bob Shennan and the powerfully efficient Mirk brought Scotland back to the brim after staring at an empty silverware cupboard for too long.

Prince Charlie did not manage it in Derbyshire, but it was rectified by Bob and the splottle-faced Mirk. What is £1 for a grandstand seat when you have such a dayful of magical stockhandling over a daunting and awesome course like the one so brilliantly natural at Chatsworth Park for the supreme championship.

But what a fright Bob and Mirk gave us on the way to the supreme in the epic work over what seemed a parish-width of historical English estate land and trees. Such a wide course in fact that each leg of the fetch had its separate gate instead of the usual system of pulling both hefts of sheep down to the one obstacle.

It was nearing the end of Bob's work shedding off ribboned ewes from unmarked ones. It is a critical stage and, as I reported in *The Scottish Farmer*, at the time, Bob was about to gather the five ribboned ones which he had dislodged to move them to the pen for the final chore "when, hell's teeth, dammit, damnation and Jek Ri'path's leggings one missed the company of the bigger mob and legged off to join them— successfully. It had all to be done again."

How that got through the Editor's vigilance I do not know but it is how we all felt. But even allowing for that stramash—it's equivalent is missing a sitter two feet from goals with the custodian lying on the ground—Bob won the award with Mirk and took the blue riband back to his 1,000-acre unit based on Farden, Turnberry, where he is in the sheep and beef business.

In the winter Mirk is separated from Bob for he goes to work for shepherd Tom Loch until the lambing at Farden entails his return. A trier for twenty years for the supreme, Bob's victory with the then eight year old Mirk was one which had been an extreme likelihood, for no dog for so long has been as consistent at local trials beforehand. From a line which fused the likes of John Richardson's Wiston Cap, Jim Hogarth's Lassie, Davie Dickson's Ben, Donald MacLeod's Garry and J. M. Wilson's Nap, Moss, Glen and Mirk without going too far back, the blue blood was there for a start before Bob Shennan tied in the practical side with everyday contracts for Mirk.

"He was quite an easy pup to break. He was shaping at five months old. He was a strong-gaun dog and determined when he was young. But he started to run quite sensibly with a lot of balance about him," said Bob who acquired the Mirk pup—out of John Nelson's little Jan—"because I always liked his sire John Richardson's Mirk and I wanted one of that kind."

"He was broken on the sheep here, and when he started, it was not long before he was running to both hands and bringing sheep. Then, like the rest, he had to do the cattle work after that. You need a good dog to shift these suckling cows and Mirk can certainly handle them."

I myself had taken greatly to Mirk after seeing him in 1975 losing only four points—a tremendous feat—to win the country's toughest trial, the Ardkinglas mountain double-run at Cairndow which that year was opened to all-comers for the first time. A collie which can win that one, even just once, merits status which some International champions do not have. Mirk was to go on to win again the following year and made his legend more of a spellbinder by completing the hat-trick in the year of his International triumph.

109

At that Chatsworth International Tom Watson, a Border shepherd, shared the top points in the Qualifying round and took the Shepherds Championship with his little Jen bitch. I wrote at the time: "She promises so much, this little 2½ year old. . . ."

Two years later when we returned to Bala for the 1980 International it was the black and white Jen which again took the supreme awards back to Scotland. With canniness and practical get-on-with-the-job sheepmanship during a get together which will be long yarned about for its manytimes superb shepherding prowess by exponents from all four nations on the final day, Tom Watson's deserved acquisition of a valleyful of trophies through his well-balanced partnership on the long-tailed mountain sheep, was rich reward for the valued effort and character he has put into the pastime over so many years.

There is a way of doing things in the sheep country. When the paths get steeper and tougher, the limbs begin to flinch at the daily climbing toils and the lungs find the wind is harder to seek for the necessary trudges, man and his dog and his sheep normally descend from the higher pastures to take on new roles on the kindlier, less demanding lower land.

Man gets his breath back and is fit for many more years to carry his crook and his lambing bag. Dog has a re-kindling of energy, biff and keenness which were perhaps beginning to melt off him following four or five years of ungrudging upland tasks. And sheep—old Blackfaces or Cheviots—liven and become more prolific on the lusher, lowland pastures.

Tom Watson, as gifted and respected a shepherd as there is, did it the other way round. For so many years a sheeptender on sometimes table-flat lowground Berwickshire grazings, Tom stepped up to the skirts of the black Lammermuirs and the hill ewe paths when little more than a handful of years short of retirement.

"A lot of folk thought I was crackers when I came here at my age," recalled Tom, "but I have really enjoyed it." It was a reference to the fact that he was sixty-seven years old and striding less regularly to the hill following official retirement.

Many decades after first journeying to sheepdog trials by bicycle or bus—with his collie sitting on his knee in the latter case—Tom was awash under silver trophies and congratulatory messages at his home at Longcroft near Lauder when I visited him in the winter of 1980/81.

A soul can go out to a trial and with luck, many bagfuls of it, get the big prize. Not often. Men like Tom Watson who for many years have been legends in their craft quietly persevere and win and bring immense enjoyment to watchers because they are steeped in shepherding know-how. They have the inborn ability to 'read' their sheep, envisaging their movements and moods and the ability too to link and balance their temperaments with that of the collies they have trained. It is what blatantly separates a stockman from a hobby trialist. It is what always brings the true stockman to the top.

It took a long, long while for Tom Watson, partnered so effectively by that great listener, the five year old Jen, to clinch the honour for there have been very few supreme champions of pensionable age. And Jen was only the fourth bitch in the previous forty years to gain the blue riband. Yet Tom started before he was twenty-one at Kelso Fair with an old bitch called Lass whose skill is still engraved in his memory. "What a beast she was, a great bold bitch."

Tom reckons he learned a lot from Nell, who twice won the International Shepherds championship. "I was very lucky to get her to start with. I got an awful lot of education through training her."

He describes his champion Jen as a "Twenty-four-hours-a-day grafter." He acquired the bright-eyed bitch when she was fifteen-months-old from Alastair Munro who bred her at his Inverness smallholding from his great Highland-blooded breeding bitch Nell. Jen's sire, Willie Jardine's Roy, is from two of Scotland's legendary dogs, Wiston Cap and David Shennan's old Maid.

Jen's biggest attribute, says Tom, is her "method"—the ability to balance a group of sheep by being in the right position at the right time and the right place to steer them. "She is easily commanded. She is a great listener and that is a grand asset in a dog.

"Method is not something you can put into a working dog. It comes from linking your temperament with that of the dog's temperament. You have to study it to get this balance. A young dog should be allowed to develop itself. They learn things in everyday work which you cannot teach them, such as balancing and anticipating the movements of sheep."

Training a working collie to come to the top in the trials world—or even in everyday sound work—"is a satisfying pastime," says Tom. So too was the feeling when he came off the big course at Bala knowing he had done well. "I suppose what made it all the more satisfying was the fact that I had been trying for so long. I will not be disappointed if I don't win the supreme championship again, but I will be trying."

So will many others, seeking that coveted blue riband.

CRAFT AND VERSE

The shepherd's daily sojourn to the hill instils into him more knowledge and gifted inventiveness than any farming College. The hirsels are classrooms and theatres of life where a cheery, natural culture comes into being.

High on the bottom rung of the Cheviot hill range with two wide-running hills to gather on his 'herding, Geoff Billingham daily commands his collies.

Come night when he has a few spare hours in the year's quieter time, he stills the collies and recaptures their style, their terrain, like rock and fern, and the fellow inhabitants of Bowmont Water—ewe, fox, owl, eagle, grouse, rabbit, mouse and butterfly—on paper or on wood.

Caught by his memory, paintings of the quiet, pastoral and wild life have been captured on paper by his self-taught ability with charcoal pencils. Such as a collie coming across greyface lambs behind a tree-trunk or sheepdogs pushing a parcel of sheep down a glen. And he also works on delicately etched panoramas of stock and countryside, adding a new dimension to the heads and shanks of his crooks.

A pencil usually goes in his pocket along with his diary when he takes to his everyday work, just to jot down a rough outline—the shape of a rock, or the impression as a waft of wind lays the grass into shape on his paths. To note, too, perhaps the expression of a ewe, ram, or even the set of a collie at work.

Geoff, a Midlander, was shepherding thirty six score of hill Cheviots on Swindon when I shared some of his time on the dimpled range above Yetholm. The emphasis in many of his drawings is on sheepdogs. Geoff has represented both England and Scotland at International level in the trials world and one of these days his prowess should bring him one of the major crowns.

Hanging above his mantlepiece was a framed etching of a collie approaching lambs behind a tree. The lambs, in fact, were sitting in a rabbit-hole and the drawing was based on reality—Geoff's old Moss dog was a stickler for looking down rabbit holes. Two of his collies which I admired many times on the trials field, Jed and Trim, gave him many ideas for drawings from their attitudes at everyday work and a very detailed etching he was doing, containing rock, fern, tree, mountain and cloud, showed their mother Meg driving ewes down a steep glen with a kennel-mate.

112

"I usually have a diary when I am on the hill and I can make rough sketches of rocks, etc.," Geoff told me. "When I am out I'm looking at the rocks and up the burns and there are many other things I see like sheep standing on a rock face which can give me ideas. With dogs, the difficulty is trying to make them look natural and get a bit of life into them. It is not easy."

Often with his pencil drawings, he will whittle the lead onto the drawing and then rub it with his fingers to produce a tonal background. Among his best works are a dramatic drawing of a Blackface ram's head; one of his blue bitch Jed, and one of a fawn looking through undergrowth.

Much more wildlife dominates the etchings he makes on his crooks, a complete departure from the normal stickmaker's tradition. Geoff paints the horn heads with touch-up black enamel. Then, with a very fine file—practically as thin as a needle and sharpened every five minutes or so—he etches out various scenes on the horn.

He has also developed the system to decorate the shank and some crooks have etchings from head to foot. Some of the birds and animals are in relief but mostly the bark has been filed off before the enamel is brushed on. One stick I saw in his household included a dramatic hunting scene right down the shank bringing in grouse, pheasants, fox, deer, weasels and even a butterfly.

There was another craftsman whose company I long enjoyed—Tom Murdie. Though long since parted from his herdings when I first met him at his cottage in Carrutherstown, Dumfriesshire, Tom had not forgotten the lore of the sheepruns he tended on the hills of Galloway, Argyllshire and Dumfriesshire.

Those who called at his whitewashed cottage where he spent an active retirement despite crippling arthritis, and listened to the yarns he told of his younger days on the hirsels, found it hard to drag themselves away. When they did, Tom did not let them leave empty-handed for he valued highly crack and company. They usually took with them one of the shepherd's whistles he carved from cattle bones.

Smaller than a matchbox the bone whistles were not just for ornamental purposes. Tom made them for over fifty years and every one had been crafted well enough for any 'herd to reach his collie on the widest of hefts.

Marrow bones were Tom's raw material and I was in his company sometimes going round butcher's shops trying to cadge them. He could get from four to six whistles off a decent sized bone. But the bone had to be sound and strong—not semi-transparent or shell-like. And ideally the sides had to be $\frac{3}{8}$ in. thick.

An hour was enough to see one whistle fashioned. It was, in fact, just a slice off the side of the bone. With the bone firmly wedged in a vice he used an ordinary hacksaw to saw off a $1\frac{1}{4}$ in. slice.

Between this and the outside he had already sawn another split (or mouth) to about $\frac{1}{4}$ in. from the bottom. This inside split was filed down by an old saw blade and any saw marks on the outside were smoothed off with a small conventional rasp. The mouth of the whistle was wider at the open end than further down.

Position of the actual hole, which was covered by the lips, was very important, according to Tom. It has to be ⅜ to ½ in. from the closed end. Any further, said Tom, and it was too far to cover with the lips. The hole—just wide enough to pass through a 3 in. darning needle—was made with a small drill and countersunk with a knife Tom had used for about fifty years.

And that was the whistle complete, except for Tom's exclusive design, an added grip at the corner in which a hole was pierced for a string or chain. When I wrote a feature on Tom for *The Scottish Farmer* in the middle of the 1960's I included a quotation: "The whole thing is a pastime now. If anybody wants a whistle made, all they need do is send me a marrow bone and they will soon have a whistle back."

Little did Tom and I realise the reaction there would be. The next week the postman brought a total of ninety parcels to Tom's door—all containing marrow bones. Some had one, some had two and some had half a dozen. Many had obviously been lying around houses or wastebins for some time and for many weeks after, the postman appeared at the end of Tom's path carrying the parcels at arms length.

Though it caused him a lot of worry at the time—he was frightened he would not manage to get whistles made for each bone-owner—the episode brought Tom into contact with people from as far as the Shetlands and Devon and he continued to write to many of them right up until his death.

Those of us who frequented sheepdog trials or passed his cottage felt a big void when Tom passed on. His skill in making the bone whistles and horn and wood-headed crooks, came from his shepherding days. He had started 'herding in 1906 near Moniaive and when he was thirteen he helped in a memorable three-day 'herding over an old drove road from Lanark taking 500 hoggs to the Corsock district of Galloway.

On their first night the men on the drove slept out at Pepperknowes, south of Lanark; the second night at Spango in Crawick Water and the third night in a farm loaning up Shinnel Water in the Penpont area of Dumfriesshire. By this time Tom's father's collie had vanished—it made off and was never seen again after being struck by a passing postman's bike.

Though he never competed at trials, Tom attended many. He was my companion many times at trials ranging from Middlesborough to Central Scotland. Anyone passing his door called to see if he was going and there was one instance when he was in full flow of reminiscences that I was twenty miles past my turn-off before I realised it. Such was his tale-telling power.

At one time the hirsels he 'herded near Beattock adjoined those of the famed J. M. Wilson during his days at Holmshaw Farm. One of the best bitches Tom ever owned was by the renowned Baty's Hemp and out of a daughter of J. M. Wilson's Toy and Dickson's Hemp. One thing, all Tom's dogs could hear his whistles. Tom even entertained his visitors to a tune on the little bone objects.

Another tuneful Dumfriesshire character from the same Moniaive airt is Joe Johnstone. Music has always been part of Joe's life on the 170-acre beef and sheep unit at Garrieston, Dunscore and all his callers are welcomed with a lullaby. Not only that—if you have time to spare, the farm's cheery gaffer will take to the bottles.

In these unmelodic times, Garrieston still keeps a lilt for the visitor. He is faced with it as soon as he comes into the steading—a beautifully worked double gate of wrought-iron with the first four bars of Brahms Lullaby.

It has been admired now for about thirty years and still gives pleasure to Joe and his family. He has gained a lot of amusement out of callers' reactions to being confronted with the gate. Those with knowledge of music can read the notes and get the melody right away "but a lot don't notice it" and others have to ask what the tune is.

Long prior to moving to Garrieston—Joe can recall clearly the days of droving lambs from the Dunscore and Corsock area to Castle Douglas when there was a drove going down the Urr Valley every fifty yards—he was among the south bothy balladeers. He plays the banjo, Jew's harp, fiddle, tin whistle, bagpipes, melodeon and the mouth organ. But a lot of people seek his services for playing wine glasses.

In his younger days, Joe was in a 'glass' band where a five-man team played up to 100 glasses with seconds and harmonisation. There are probably few left now with the ability to play wine glasses, but at a ceilidh during the International Sheep Dog Trials at Lockerbie in 1976, over 400 people truly appreciated his capabilities.

His pride is a set of antique glasses which have been ground into tune. There are twenty-four glasses in this set, giving three scales. With wet fingers and a light touch circling round the outside of the glasses, Joe can produce many melodies from the set.

He is also a gifted prose writer. In fact he is often inclined to send his entries to sheepdog trial secretaries in verse. This one was sent to Willie Welsh, secretary of the Doon Valley trials near Dalmellington, when he entered that event one year:

"Dear Wull I here enclose the cash
That I may come and hae a bash
On July's six and twentieth day
At droving sheep on Smithston's brae
There through the bogs and spret to sail
I'll bring young Jess and also Gail
May everything so smoothly go
With kind regards, yours truly, Joe."

There was another poet in that area—or rather a poetess—whom I featured once and whose words are worth recalling. Even as a toddler Ella McMillan wandered with her father Sam McMillan who was once shepherd at Castlefairn, Knocksting and Loch Rennie on a Moniaive tending of sixty-eight score ewes and sixty-four Galloway cows.

Ella always wished she had been a boy and a shepherd. She did the next best thing. At eighteen years of age she was a student nurse at the Western Generai Hospital in Edinburgh. But she never forgot Castlefairn and penned these words one night in hospital which she sent to her parents. There was no title. I reckoned 'The Good Shepherdess' was appropriate.

> I sit by a sick man's bed tonight
> I watch him lose a long brave fight,
> I think back to the days, when as a bairn
> I climbed the hills at Castlefairn
>
> I followed Dad o'er dyke and stell
> Through heather, bracken and sweet bluebell
> To save some lamb or 'cowpit' sheep
> From neath the corbie's cruel beak
>
> Thank you dad, for now I see
> What your skill and patience has done for me
> Without 'O' levels or honours degree
> You passed on so much knowledge to me
>
> Not now the soft green turf beneath my feet
> Bracken green, with scent so sweet
> No faithful collie to hear me speak
> I tend mankind instead of sheep

There were worthies with words elsewhere too. Meeting John MacDonald was like meeting one of these homely characters from the old-time *Wizard* or *Rover*. His cosy abode, a showman's caravan in the midst of a Morayshire forest, could be no more appropriate for such a worthy and pleasant soul in dour wintertime at the end of January 1970.

A winter time's crack with John MacDonald could never be long enough. There are the folk-tales he will tell, the ballads he will sing, and the yarns he relates of his rovin' on the kind farmlands of his native airt.

All fit neatly into the niche he had carved as Scotland's 'Singing Molecatcher.' And thereby hangs a tale—or rather 20,000 tails. For that was the tally of John's fifty years of mowdie catching when I met in with him. It once earned him the title of Britain's champion.

He was also once Scotland's diddling (form of mouth music) champion, one of the highlights of his very active line in folk singing, ballad writing and entertaining, most of which was for charity—and enjoyment.

Each year John MacDonald took to the road with his wife and went as far south as Wigtownshire and Dumfriesshire with his children's folklore puppet theatre.

He also took to the road when he was thirteen—to run away from the school at Dava which he had attended "when I had to." He took to the grouse moors to help the keepers.

Around 1920 he had his first spell catching moles. Mr Semple of Merrytown, Nairn gave him the chance. "For killing moles we got one penny a tail but skins were good value, making from one to two shillings each. Now nobody wants the skins," said John who still cycled ten to fifteen miles a day on a 1919 cycle when I visited him.

Born on his father's tenanted farm at Bogney, Dunphail, John would be about the last catcher in the county to use traps. When skins were in the fashion in the 1920's, he sent 5,000 in a season—all from a twenty-mile radius—when a furrier ran a 'champion molecatcher' competition.

It was on his tramps round molehills that John MacDonald—"I have been singing all my life"—got the inspiration to write folk songs, many of them known all over the world through records, tapes and radio programmes.

"I cannot make up a song if anybody asks me. It just has to come. But when something happens I can make it up at once. Getting the tune is the worst part. I think of all the tunes and try and get something different," John told me at his home at Pitgaveny, near Elgin.

Among the fine ballads penned and sung by the 'Singing Molecatcher' are 'The Rovin' Ploughboy,' 'The Wandering Shepherd Laddie,' 'Bonnie Woods of Pitgaveny,' 'Dava Hills,' 'Cawdor's Bonnie Woods,' and 'The Wild Nicht.'

The tales behind the writing of the songs are interesting. During the last century a great storm swept Dava moor and a trainload of Highland cattle was buried in the snow. Some forty were frozen. That is how 'The Wild Nicht' came to be written. And when it was featured in a broadcast in Canada, a lady in Newfoundland wrote to John telling him it was her late father who had been engine driver on the fated train.

John once noticed an elderly lady crying in a bus coming back from Inverness. On asking her troubles he found she had been seeing her grandson off to Canada and he had said he would miss the 'Bonnie Woods of Cawdor.' So that was another ballad.

John collected thousands of folksongs which ensured his popularity at folk nights. His melodeon was known throughout the country and his words will be heard down through succeeding generations.

REBUILDING TRADITION

In the higher parts of Scotland and other areas of the UK the dykes mark the boundaries between fields or farms. They extend to thousands of miles and much of the dyking is over a century old, especially in the south-west of Scotland. The skill of the dykers is still passed on and it is a satisfying and well-paid profession for those who have taken it up.

Beside a quiet hill road through sheep country steeped in the lore of the Covenanters I have watched the drystane dykers of Auldgirth rebuild part of South Scotland's upland farming history.

Dyker Charlie Jardine—fourth generation of his family to carry on the craft—looked at his four men rebuilding a 100-year old dyke and said: "These dykes are really monuments to the men who build them."

Only a few hundred yards away on this hillside above Irongray on the Dumfriesshire-Galloway border, sculptor/artist Henry Moore has also left for posterity some of his modernistic creations dotted over the knowes.

But to the country dweller there is no doubt which leaves the more fitting and lasting impression. For these dykes—and there are over 7,000 miles of drystane work in Kirkcudbrightshire alone—have the hallmark of a skill unspoiled by modern machinery and materials.

The dyker of today relies on the tools of yesterday, his hands—which will handle twelve tons of stone a day—his hammers, builder's line, foot rule and a frame.

"If you can stick it for the first three years then you can learn enough to be a good dyker," said Charlie Jardine back in 1968 when I watched him rebuilding that dyke near Irongray. "But even after that you are always learning something. There is no scarcity of work for a young man who can build a good dyke."

It had been in 1924 that Charlie lifted his first whinstone. That job was at Benbuie, about six miles above Moniaive in Dumfriesshire. His second job that year was on an 800-yard stretch on the hill between Skinford and Muil, only half a mile from that 1968 contract at Cornlees on the Speddoch Estate. "My father built that dyke. We walked two miles to the place every day for three months and in that time were stopped only two days because of rain," he said.

Today that dyke stands as erect as it was when the job was finished many decades ago.

It is believed drystane dyking—building walls in natural local stone without cement or mortar—began in Kirkcudbrightshire around 1710 and spread throughout the country. I have even come across a drystane dyke within a few minutes motor run of Auckland's busy International airport in New Zealand and in the tree-covered hills of Cape Breton, Nova Scotia. There are some dyking worthies who reckon the test for a good dyke is their ability to wheel a barrow along the top and a tale was told some years ago in the weekly *Southern Reporter* about a middle-aged dyker who once asked his Church Minister what the initials D. D. after his name implied. He was told they signified 'Doctor of Divinity.' A few days later John the dyker had to sign some documents in the presence of the Minister and he added the letters D. D. "What does that mean?" queried the Minister. "Och, just drystane dyker," replied John. "You cannot do that," said the Minister, "it's not a profession." John came back: "Y're richt Minister, it's no a profession—it's an art."

It was certainly an art in the Jardine family. Charlie Jardine's uncle James retired in 1966 at the age of seventy-six. The great-grandfather, William, lived at Lochhill in Glencairn parish; grandfather James at Townhead, Dunscore, and his father William was also in the parish where the present Mr Jardine was brought up.

Family records show prices in the old days working out at from 6d to 9d a yard—and a man's average length a day is still around six yards.

In these old days dykers spun out their working year by rabbit-catching and draining. "Now there is not much of that going on. I used to do these seasonal jobs myself but now we are dyking all the year round," said Charlie Jardine who had four workmen helping him on that Cornlees contract.

Mostly the job nowadays is rebuilding dykes. Any new dykes are mostly for local authorities in connection with re-alignment of roads. Forestry encroachment in the hills and glens has meant the end of a lot of dry walls.

"You have to get the job right to make a dyke stand," said Charlie. "A lot are thrown together and are down in no time. If the stones are well locked together and are hearted well, the dyke will stand for a century."

He reckoned a man could average about six yards a day for a 4 ft 6 in high dyke. "If he builds this he is turning out six tons of stone a day. On some dykes it may be more and could be less. But a good dyker doing six yards is not wasting any time."

Mr Jardine followed the traditional Galloway dyking specifications. On the Cornlees contract which entailed rebuilding some 1,500 yards, the men firstly stripped out a length of old dyke. With four workers plus Charlie himself, they found it ideal to take a 20-25 yard stretch in hand, laying out the stones and then clearing the foundation.

In some places it is not suitable to rebuilt on old foundations, but when this is possible, the new dyke should be stronger than ever.

Closely followed, with a few modifications, was the specification for a 4 ft 6 in dyke described in his book *Dry Stone Walling* by the late

Colonel Rainsford-Hannay of Kirkdale who started the Stewartry Drystane Dyking Committee in 1938. It was re-formed at the start of the 1960's and is now very active with a popular competition every second year at Gatehouse of Fleet. It also helped to organise training courses through the Agricultural Training Board.

Specifications from the book, which was reprinted a few years ago, are: "Height to be 4 ft 6 ins. Foundation to be 32 in. wide and the base 26 in. wide at the lift or immediately above the foundation stones. From there build to taper gradually to 14 in. wide at the top of the Double, which is to be 3 ft 6 in. above the grass. The Double to have both sides brought up together, having the stones properly blocked, laid close together well hearted and packed in the centre, every stone doing its duty by its neighbour. The outer stones to lie with their ends gradually inward, so as to stretch into the dyke as far as possible for the better binding of the work. Water-born stones are not to be used.

"The Double to have one set of throughbands 21 in. above the grass at one yard centres, projecting slightly on each side. The cover band stones on top of the Double to project 2 in. on either side. From there each stone of the single to diminish gradually in width to the top, no stones to be less than 10 in. high and all well locked together."

Dykers move little from the dykesides to pick up stones. All the stones will find a place somewhere in the wall. When I watched Charlie Jardine and his Auldgirth men toil in 1968, hard blue whinstone was the material though further south in the Stewartry there is a lot of granite.

The whinstone gives a good clean break when stones are being split, whereas granite, said Charlie, is inclined to break into knots.

The foundation is laid with large stones and well hearted to keep them in position. Lines are then set up on frames made to dyke specifications. They are used for guiding in the 'batter' (or tapering) of the dyke and for ensuring a level top-line.

In the first course a double row of stones is laid with the longer ends on the inside. Solid hearting, one of the secrets of a good dyke, is with hard stones. "If this part is not done properly the stones sit down in the centre and can slip in," said Charlie.

The throughbands need a good firm bed on the lower stones. Stones are laid on top of the 'throughs' to about 3ft 6 in. from the ground where the width will be about 12-15 ins. Cover bands are placed on and then the topping with the copestones.

"The top should be set straight up. If you have them lying about you cannot key them tight together," said Charlie. "If the topstone is a bit loose a pinstone hammered in will tighten it."

On a steep brae topping is always against the lie of the hill. In the same circumstances when rebuilding a dyke a 'raggle' end is built every six yards to keep the dyke from 'creeping down' behind the builder.

One of the main aspects to watch, said Charlie, is topping a little at a

120

time. "Leave it until a section is ready and you will get a nice run on top.

At corners or gates, the builders begin from a pillar or 'cheek' and get their alignment from there. When building a 'cheek' they have to tie front stones back with a long stone running back into the double.

The Auldgirth dykers mostly used a 4½-5 lb. mash hammer for breaking the whinstone. Less than that and they could not make much impression on the hard stone. During the building of the dyke, pinning usually kept up with the wall's progress. The pins—small wedging stones—were tapped into small gaps and besides making the dyke rabbit-proof added strength.

A rolling stone gathers expense. There is no doubt about that according to Charlie who, in over fifty years at the profession, built enough dykes to stretch from Dumfries to Glasgow.

I watched him again in 1975 doing some more dyking in Dumfriesshire. He had this advice for farmers and shepherds with walls on their property. "Don't walk past any stones which have been rubbed off a dyke by an animal or have fallen. Put them back. It will stop it becoming a gap, then maybe even the dyke coming out like a pack of cards, leading to an expensive rebuilding job."

By this time Charlie had become perhaps the country's most travelled dyker going to all parts of Scotland through his tutoring at Agricultural Training Board Courses and College classes. These had ranged from Arran to Caithness, passing on hints to farmers and employees who sought enough knowledge to make a decent maintenance job at home.

If they could do this, he emphasised, undoubtedly they were going to save on expensive bills. What had been 1s. 8d a yard for rebuilding dykes when Charlie started to follow the trade and build the first of his seventy-two miles of dyking was around £2 a yard in 1975. One can only guess where it stands now in this inflationary era.

In his talks at these courses Charlie told his listeners the important thing was to get a man onto the job right away if a gap appeared in a wall.

"The thing is to try and spare a day or two in the Spring for men to go round the dykes and keep in the 'tops' and any small gap that has been knocked down."

A lot of people think they can go along and throw any stones on a dyke and this will make a sound wall. "This is absolutely wrong" said Charlie. "Another thing is that some people, perhaps going to fill gaps, never look at the dyke that is standing. They just lift the first stones they come to. They never think of starting from where the damage began. They sometimes just start with big stones at the bottom and finish with small stones at the top. This will never last. It will be no time at all before sheep are back and knocking the small ones out.

"Study the dyke thoroughly. Clear the whole thing out right from where the trouble has started, put small stones in first and big ones to finish off."

Another aspect where participants sometimes went wrong on the courses, said Charlie, was in hearting and packing the wrong way. "It is like a man—if he doesn't get his dinner or something to put in his middle, he will never carry out a job. So a dyke must be well packed and hearted with stones kept level and they must not hang at the nose.

"You have to keep the centre up and that turns the water. If water gets in the centre and it becomes frosty it spreads the dyke out. You will find old dykes built centuries ago which are dry as anything in the middle, even although there has been no cement or anything about it."

Though his dyking work took him to many different areas with a variety of stone type, the method he advised for building was always the same. "Once you have learned the job you will never forget it".

Helen B. Cruickshank was inspired to write the following lines after observing the durability of Dry Stane Dykes.

Dry Stane Dykes

Oor forebears biggit weel withooten fyke
The cottar hoose, the byre, the drystane dyke.
Their horny hands were skeely, hard and strang,
Their life was simple, kennin richt frae wrang.

They helped a neebor fan the gudeman ailed,
At hairst or ploo, or fan the crops had failed;
Men o few words, but trusty freens in need,
Hard work their portion, an giff-gaff their creed.

Their gable wa's o biggins may be gane,
Dinged doon by bruckle brick, synthetic stane;
But roon the hills and haughs, the native kye
Still graze in peace in dyked security.

And lang may Scotland haud her ain traditions,
Yet claim her richtfu place in League o Nations.
Wha kens? Her wecht, the throwband stane micht be
Tae bind a shoogly warld in Amity.

(Throwband-stane: The long balancing stone thrust out on either side without which the dyke would fall, since it contains no mortar)

MEN OF STEEL

*Some think the flockmaster has a leisurely job. Perhaps they only see him
as they drive up the glen roads—a figure calmly walking among his stock.
But there are hard tasks to accomplish whether in the line of duty or
relaxation and there are many moments when the hill man's physical
durability is severely challenged.*

The high land is not for the weak. But there are those tougher and of
greater endurance than others.

Joss Naylor for instance. Joss, wiry sheepman without a crook, has
strode, raced, duelled and mastered the roof of our land.

Far above the contours of his Herdwick heaths and the steep crags
and lonesome tarns where his three year old wether sheep graze near the
dozen remaining yew trees of the old Copeland Forest, he chiselled a
legend at the foot of the clouds.

That is the place, atop the mist line and the last of the fell sheep
paths, where the quiet deeds of mountain runners—and Joss, able farmer
and thought-provoking conversationalist has the respect of them all—are
assured due recognition. They in turn respect the dour peaks, sometimes
their solitary companions in their intriguing joust with nature.

Broken into the Lakeman's sheep ways further up valley, Joss developed
on the tops of Bowderdale Farm—it lifts itself up to 2,800 ft around Red
Pike and Scoat Fell which in turn are looked down upon by other South
Cumbrian peaks—his own ways with the Herdwick sheep breed and the
Rough Fell/Swaledale crosses.

And he lit off when time permitted to push his lithe 9½ stone frame,
wracked many times by injuries and bone displacements, to the near
unbelievable extent of running and conquering in a summer day seventy-
two peaks all over 2,000 ft in twenty-three hours eleven minutes. Which
means 40,000 ft of ascent and a distance of 108 miles on foot in under a
day.

The way Joss approached the feat and trained for it through other
mountain marathons makes for more uncanny reading for those of us
who pech after clambering a dyke. And when he had jogged that 108
miles he clipped sheep for three weeks and then turned out to win a
twenty-two mile fell race during which he did 8,500 ft of climbing. He has
even romped up Ben Nevis in under an hour.

Herdwick sheep, the Welsh fourteen three-thousands, Rough Fell
crosses, the Pennine Way record run, black suckler cows, the Pike Peaks

battle in Colorado—there are two Joss Naylors, a fusion of fleet footedness, mountain sureness and fell country stockmanship.

Joss was stocking a thousand sheep on Bowderdale when I listened to his story in November 1975, the year of one of his greatest achievements. It was in June that year that he jogged up and down those seventy-two peaks in under twenty-four hours, a mighty travelogue round a big whack of the Lake District including Skiddaw, Saddleback, Helvellyn and Sca Fell—and sixty-eight others. Previous to that attempt he had managed sixty-three of these 'two thousanders' in a day two years before during bad weather—again relying not on the much vaunted health drinks and foods but mostly on the cakes made by his wife Mary.

"He's like a dustbin," she said. Every time he comes in the house he picks up something to eat."

"It takes a lifetime to put together a run like that," said Joss, recalling that 108-mile day which had begun at seven minutes past seven in the morning and ended at eighteen minutes past six. There was also the training which began when he took an hour off the previous record for running the ten highest mountains in the Lake District. Then he had another ten days solid training doing 200 miles of hard running on the fells, taking as much liquid as he could—much of it from the burns.

On a wet day he took half an hour off the previous record for the four 'three thousand' Lake peaks—he did forty-five miles of running in seven hours thirty minutes—then competed in a race in Wales doing four peaks of over a thousand metres. He lopped quarter of an hour off that record. The following week he won the Ennerdale Fell race for the eighth time and then came that twenty-four hour session before settling down to the sheep shearing.

Joss surprised me by saying he never carried a shepherd's crook. What is an essential aid to others was an obvious impediment for his gait during his sheep work, for Joss, in shorts and shoes, did his gathering runs to the farthest point himself. His speed in doing so at that time meant he could gather all the sheep in eight hours over a big area of ground.

His running brought many struggles with the elements, so much so that after some runs his hands were swollen with the blood running down his arms. In 1975, trips took him to the Pikes Peak marathon in Colorado, U.S.A., an altitude event which started at six and a half thousand feet and was mostly at 14,000 ft. He finished sixth from 374 starters.

Joss has completed the Ben Nevis-Scafell-Snowdon climbs in eleven hours fifty-four minutes including travelling time between them, having climbed the Fort William mountain in fifty minutes from sea level. Unless traffic regulations were broken I could not see that record being beaten.

Joss was forty years old at the time I spent several interesting hours at his fireside and he reckoned the ideal age for marathon running was thirty-five to thirty-seven. "On one of these twenty-four-hour runs you have to have so much going for you. You don't have to have a bad patch because it is run at such a pace. And you've got to have the ability to completely switch off. You suffer. On the last five or six hours on the seventy-two peaks I had a tremendous pain in my back, possibly through a chill in the kidneys. The body takes a tremendous hammering. You have to know that you can do it."

I have also been long acquainted with two other cheery marathon men from a different sphere. Balanced lightly on their feet—shod in rough home-made moccasins of leather or jute bagging—and strong and supple of wrist, the likes of John Edgar and Willie Lawson take only a minute to harvest a valuable thick crop which has taken a year to mature.

Artists at their own back-aching but precision craft among the upland sheep fanks or in low-ground flockmasters' modern facilities, they thrive, banter and persevere in the midsummer weeks to the sounds, smells and rhythms of sheep shearing.

Taking anywhere from thirty to sixty 'blows' with their machine clippers over Blackface, Cheviot or various crosses, and making every move of hand, knee and foot count, they are among the ever-growing band of shearing men whose job can take them to many faraway lands.

On a June Saturday in 1977 in front of a packed and enthusiastic market ring in Castle Douglas, Kirkcudbrightshire, they romped their way into the record books with the highest clipping tally by two U.K. men in a nine-hour run—654 sheep sheared, 99 above the previous best.

While boosting local funds for the Cancer Research Campaign that day, the two men who have a vast experience of the shearing game here and overseas, brought a touch of glamour to an everyday summer sheepman's job. It is one unlikely ever to become automated, apart from the shearing tackle.

It was a fascinating day. Willie, from Wigtown and a former U.K. record speed man—he shore 284 sheep in a 7½ hour run but has often done over 300 on farms—had always a joke for the onlookers despite the odd kicker, for some sheep began to feel the effects of empty bellies, having been housed the night before. Following a medical check before their record bid Willie quipped: "I was declared sound in wind and limb, but not mentally."

John, from Newfield, Dalry, took the odd swig from what looked like a sheep drenching canister and donned a head sweatband. As they set off Willie opened up some chewing gum—not so much for chewing but to stick between his teeth for concentration and to keep moisture in his mouth. Both men went through a fair amount of salt tablets during their day on the boards. John had four changes of clothing.

By dinner-gong, the pair had a 412 total up on the blackboard—they had previously gunned 151 of the hill Blackfaces before breakfast. An ever-growing ringside stayed on. The next break after the hour's dinner was at a quarter to four when they had swept to 532 hoggs. Twenty minutes after the re-start they hiked past the six year old record of 555 head with

Willie's long blows baring sheep number 556.

The lads had been aiming all along for the 600-650 mark and the last run saw them in full steam again with encouragement from the ringsiders, especially in the last ten minutes as they were cajoled to reach the 650 tally. They did it too with one of the latter John Edgar hoggs doffed of its wool in fifty-three seconds.

"You never get tired of the job," Willie told me a few weeks afterwards when I again caught up with him on the shearing boards at a farm in Dumfriesshire. "You are striving for something that will never happen—perfection. I don't think there is a season in which you don't improve on the previous one. By the time I'm sixty I'll maybe be good." He was forty-seven then.

Both these shearers wore home-made moccasins for the necessary grip on the clipping boards to help turn and steer the sheep. A jerk on the trip-cord of the electric shearers—usually hanging handily about 1½-2 ft off the floor—whipped the combs into action and the men were off on a swift task whose movements and style were always the same.

It is a rhythm in which they mould themselves to the sheep in a technique developed by that New Zealand maestro Godfrey Bowen whom I had the pleasure of meeting and interviewing in both his native land and in our own. "A good shearer can be likened to a good dancer or skater," said Godfrey.

One who has the attributes is Border shepherd's son Tom Wilson. Bare-footed and topped by a roary red and white headband Tom clipped stylishly through ten ewe hoggs in under twenty minutes for a mighty victory in the Highland Shears competition at the Highland Show in 1978.

This is one of the highlights of the year for Scottish clippers and is on the U.K. championship circuit. That day in June 1978 Tom ploughed the fleeces off his ten big North Country hoggs in nineteen minutes, thirteen seconds in a fast, furious and tensely close final.

Tom is capable of gunning about 300 biggish sheep in a working day and has even shorn 360 small Welsh beasts. He was, that day, taking his first major title during a shearing spell at the time which would see him with a tally of about nine to ten thousand U.K. sheep before doffing another seven thousand or so in Norway followed by a New Zealand start in December.

Many of Scotland's ablest machine shearers shift to Norway to clip the mountain and valley lambs. It can entail squads fleecing about 3,500 lambs apiece for a farm co-operative during a six to eight week stay from September into October. The lambs are shorn before slaughter and the breeding stock too are cleared of their wool before going inside sheds for the winter.

As one whose written record is five old ewes a day with hand shears—I was a 'blademan' in shearing lingo—I envy the young supple clippers their healthy life, especially when they meet in with the yarning musterers from the New Zealand back country.

One soul I did not envy, however, was shepherd Tony McGarva in 1968 when he was recovering from a seventeen-hour blizzard ordeal during which he trekked nearly ten miles through waist-deep snow to reach safety.

That wild February day he pointed up to his 2,800 ft snow-hidden hirsel—one of the most exposed and highest in Dumfriesshire—and told me: "It was something I never want to go through again. I knew that if I had panicked or even stopped for a rest I was finished. I had to keep going and it was only my knowledge of the landmarks which saved me."

The story of how Tony, then a forty-year-old bachelor, tried unsuccessfully to find a burn which would have led him easily to another shepherd's cottage; how he had to leave two exhausted collies behind on the hill; and of how his knowledge of local dykes, fences and burns finally brought him to safety was one of the most remarkable shepherding dramas in the area.

The two collies which he left in the snow arrived back three days later.

At that time Tony, a shepherd all his working days, had herded the exposed 1,500-acre Queensberry hirsel at outlying Kinnelhead, near Beattock for six years. He had thirty-one score Blackface ewes and 8½ score of hoggs. It was a fine morning when he footed off for his six hefts with three collies, Nell, Moss and Jed.

"There was no warning of what was to come," Tony told me as he sat beside the Kinnelhead fireplace after his ordeal. "I had seen three of the hefts and was at another. The mist settled and a snowstorm started. Everything was obliterated within ten minutes."

When he realised the dangers and the necessity of making back to the farmstead he could see no landmarks at all and the snow by then was between fifteen and eighteen inches deep all over. "It was impossible to get bearings as everything like drains, burns and other landmarks were level with snow. Everything was completely covered."

From early morning until five o'clock Tony hunted for a familiar sign in the thick mist and blinding snow. In near darkness he came to the side of the vast Ae Forest which he recognised. His two rough-haired collies Nell and Moss were exhausted with the snow sticking to them. Moss was left at a march dyke and then Nell too had to be abandoned, though Tony carried her for some time. He left each of them some bread from his piece and he stumbled on with Jed, a bitch whose bare skin made her more mobile. Tony had also the sense to keep some of his piece for later on.

Having found the forest he began the long trudge down past cairns and gills which he recognised though he could not see a thing. At 2.20 a.m.—17½ hours after he set off—he staggered into the house.

"I just knew I had to keep on. I had to move all the time or I was finished," said Tony. "If I had lost the place, panicked or stopped for a rest that was that, for the snow was up to my waist at many places."

127

Fellow shepherds, doctors and policemen had practically given up hope of finding him in such conditions.

Two days later—four days after setting off for the hill—Nell scampered back to the farm and Moss arrived at a neighbouring shepherd's cottage.

Both typical hill collies kept in the best of condition, they soon got over their experience. There are dogs of iron as well as men of steel.

DOGS OF LEGEND

Great working sheepdogs—great whether by dint of their work or their character—do not need materialistic memorials. Their names are handed down and spoken of daily, with awe and respect.

The legendary collies of the past are as well known to today's shepherding generations as are the current victors. And those which came to the fore in my own decade and a half in the business—valued workers such as Wiston Cap, Gilchrist's Spot, McKnight's Gael, Shennan's Maid and others—have left imprints in the record books which can never be erased.

The entry No. 33154—"Wiston Cap, dog, rough B. and W., 28/9/63"—in the International Sheep Dog Society stud book is the beginning of one of the biggest legends of all time in collie lore. No collie in the last few decades has had such an influence on the shepherding world. His breeding can be traced to every pastoral country in the world.

The foundation of his own memorial was his prowess so gloriously exemplified in 1965 in Cardiff with a supreme championship run at the International trials at twenty-one months of age which no one will forget. This was later built on by his clearly identifiable progeny. So many hundreds of them—so many champions locally and nationally—in the trials world and on sheep and cattle ground far removed from the trials sphere. A dogman knows a Wiston Capper as clearly as a Rolls Royce differs from a Mini.

The big prick-eared collie which shepherd John Richardson picked up as a five-week-old pup and was to produce one of the most influential bloodlines ever to hit any sector of the livestock industry, became an emblem and a fashion. He is flaunted worldwide on the International Sheep Dog Society's ties and membership badges through the classic pose that he held in his approach to sheep.

There are scores of stick-makers in Scotland who, each winter, carve Cap's outline on the nose of their crooks, and many an amateur artist has a go at copying Cap's power-pose.

It was during John Richardson's herding at Lyne in that great collie county of Peeblesshire that Wiston Cap first started a working career that was to bring him fame. His mother was a sound hill bitch, Walter Hetherington's Fly, a daughter of J. M. Wilson's Bill 11 out of Jack Hogarth's Lassie. Bill 11 goes back through the far-famed Whitehope Nap, the power worker, to Kirk's Nell, the mother of many champions.

129

On the paternal side, Wiston Cap is off John Richardson's own Cap which goes back through the likes of J. M. Wilson's great Glen, again to Kirk's Nell. Throughout the breeding there is much of the blaze-faced Whitehope Cap. An old shepherd once told John the best dog he had ever seen was Wilson's Cap "so I thought I would breed with him. I started crossing back and forward on the Cap lines until I got the half white-headed dog—that was my own old Cap. There were sixteen crosses of Wilson's Cap in him," said John.

He had also been impressed with Wilson's Bill 11 which he once used for a while in his herding days. "I like him very much," said John. "Wiston Cap's mother had a lot of good things in her and knowing that she was a Bill 11 as well, it was one of the reasons for getting the young Cap."

The late J. M. Wilson told me much about the legendary Whitehope Cap which he got at 18 months old and which was undoubtedly THE breeding dog in Britain during the war years when there were no trials where shepherds could see prospective stud dogs. Today every other champion can be traced back to him.

He was a rough-coated dog with a lot of white, especially on the head and front. But what a command he had over bulk of sheep, say those who saw him. It was by this word of mouth that his reputation spread to the shepherds in those days.

One of his daughters also made the record books for all times—Kirk's Nell which produced forty-four pups in her lifetime, including three which took first, second and third places at an International supreme championship, one of these records which might never be equalled.

In his first trials season at under two years old Wiston Cap won thirty shillings in prizes at local events—and that International title in 1965. That run will always be recalled by John "as though it were yesterday. Cap had a good outrun, right to his sheep, although the judges had points deducted from me at the top. His return for the second lot of sheep was perfection (this is what everybody always talks about). He had a good fetch and drive to the second drive gate where some sheep went past the obstacle. Knowing that I had been wrong the previous day in the shepherds' class by pressing the Welsh sheep too much I stood back in the supreme and they more or less shed off themselves."

I have seen Cap many times at work on his homegrounds, from the glaur of a turnip field at Lyne farm to other units where John has shepherded. One of the most impressive occasions was after a trial when we had gone to John's home and suppered and he showed Cap's full worth on the hills. He sent him a quarter of a mile where the big dog gathered a field of sheep and with one wheep he was instructed to leave this batch of ewes and go to the next field and put the ewes there together. This happened two more times until Cap could hardly be seen a mile away.

After that 1965 International victory Cap went on to become the most prolific breeder since no-one knows. I remember once when calling at the International Sheep Dog Society offices, then in Darlington, seeing that his index card—needed when pups were registered from him—was just left permanently out of the file. Much of the material he left came to the fore including several supreme championship winning sons and now grandsons. But it would take a computer to work out how many trials have been won by his blood and how many of his progeny have run at National events.

There was a day when John Richardson was offered £50 for Wiston Cap's sire, old Cap. After his International win he was offered £500 for the winner himself. But you do not buy these kind of dogs. Meanwhile collies not fit to scratch the old maestro's famous lugs are selling at over the four figure mark.

Cap in his prime and his glory driving sheep—five, twenty or a drove—with shoulder movements, on trials field or hill ground was a memorable sight. As much a thrill as when he instantly responded to any command tailed off with the had-to-be-obeyed phrase from Jock, "ca-PU."

I last saw Cap working in December 1975 on the heights above Garvald in the Lammermuirs where John was shepherding. The lugs which had launched a legend were drooped a bit by then. "His lungs are still sound enough, his hearing is not too bad and he can still see well. He is O.K. on top but his old legs won't go fast enough," said John who, with his son John jnr., shared some big Blackface sheep rakes on 3,000 acres of Johnscleugh farm.

Wiston Cap now lies at rest on these acres facing the sun. His memorial is in everyday crack about his deeds and his progeny.

It is the same with the white-flecked Spot, double Scottish champion and International supreme runner-up of John Gilchrist who has left an indelible mark here and abroad. His entry in the ISDS stud book also became one of the most thumbed for those seeking aristocratic blood which included four International champions in his grand-sire's pedigree—Wallace's Moss, Scott's old Kep, Sandy Millar's Spot and J. M. Wilson's Craig.

The rough coated Spot ran in his first trial at about two years old at Kinross. "Some say he might not be as good as my old Spot," said John referring to the grand-sire with which John gained the supreme award in 1947. "But I think he is better. He is far easier to handle."

John Gilchrist probably still shakes his head when he thinks of the 1966 International at Chester and remembers the error he made. Heavy rain on his glasses impaired his vision at the first gate of the drive during the shepherds championship and he asked Spot to turn the sheep into the cross-drive before he had put them through the gate. "Spot looked back at me after my command—he knew I had made a mistake," said John.

Earlier that Autumn he had won the Scottish National Championship for the second year running with Spot, whose dam, P. McGregor Hepburn's Nan 111, is off J. M. Wilson's Moss and W. S. Hetherington's Ann, so bringing in the blood of Wilson's Mirk, Purdie's Tam and—once again—Kirk's Nell, the daughter of J. M. Wilson's Cap and McCaskie's Moss. Kirk's Nell also figures on the paternal side.

In gaining that second Scottish championship crown at Kilmartin, Spot was awarded 197 points out of 200. No other Scottish champion since then has lost as few points though Stuart Davidson came near it in 1980 when his black and white Ben spilled only five marks.

Gilchrist's Spot blood has won countless trials and championships and I have seen two of his daughters, Fleet and Bet, win the championship and reserve at the U.S. Championships in 1973. Like Wiston Cap, his name is handed down as is everyday knowledge.

So too is the 'greatest bitch of all time,' an accolade given by my good friend Eric Halsall to Thomson McKnight's wonderful worker Gael in his classic book *Sheepdogs—my Faithful Friends* (Patrick Stephens Ltd., Cambridge). Eric enthuses for many pages over Gael and I too will not forget the day in 1967 when among drizzling mist she culminated nine years of trials running with the supreme International Championship.

The smooth-coated worker was only the second bitch in twenty-nine years to win the supreme honour—and not many do it at eleven years old. Worthington's Juno won the International in 1963 and before that we have to go back to 1938 with William Wallace's Jed from the collie stronghold at Otterburn.

For Gael, the Stirling triumph was her due. She had represented Scotland over the previous seven years, her best up to then being the winning of the Scottish title in 1964. She was reserve supreme in 1965 and her daughter Dot 111 partnered Gael in winning the Scottish doubles championship for three years. They capped the Stirling event by taking the supreme International pairs award.

Gael had begun her career cycling to work. Or at least her owner Thomson McKnight did the cycling while Gael got a lift on the bike. "When I was at that time managing a dairy farm near East Kilbride we had no sheep from the beginning of April until the start of October. When I wanted to run at trials during the summer I had to bike two miles if I wanted to train Gael on sheep. So I carried her there on the bike and she ran back," said Thomson.

That dairy farm was Gael's birthplace for Thomson had her mother Dot, a collie he got off David Young, Straid, New Cumnock, who was possibly the man most responsible for getting Thomson started. Gael was born on 4th April and when the hoggs came to winter on the farm in October she was taken out and "worked right away. She was more or less trained on wintering hoggs and a lot of dairy cattle. She had a lot of beasts to shift for there were two farms about five miles apart and they had to be walked between the units."

132

Up to the time of Gael's arrival, Thomson had not been running much at trials, possibly only at twenty a year. He had started in 1957. Some of these runs were with Gael's mother Dot, a daughter of Swan's Jim—which went to New Zealand—and David Young's Tib. It was when Dot died at about four years old that Thomson decided to hold on to Gael who at that time was a near certainty to head for New Zealand too.

The Kiwis' loss was Britain's gain in no small measure. For in her nine years of trialling Gael won over £1,000 and has left a bloodline including several champions in demand all over the world.

The paternal side contributed more to her future fortunes. She was off Whitehope Nap—"the most classy, stylish thing I have ever seen" said Thomson—the 1955 Scottish champion and supreme runner-up. There were at least five crosses of Wilson's Cap in Gael.

Thomas McKnight and his collies moved to Glencartholm beside the River Esk in Canonbie, Dumfriesshire in 1960. He had originated from a Lanarkshire mining village and was a shepherd, a farm worker and a farm manager before getting Glencartholm.

Ask Thomson what was Gael's main attribute and he will tell you: "Her nature. But she was very powerful and never stuck at anything. She was always willing. It did not matter what the sheep were like. If they were good she would behave and if they were bad she would stick in.

"I learned a lot with her,"said Thomson. "But to start with I was a raw character with very little experience. I wish I had her now." Thomson went on to achieve more fame with some of his other collies, Dot, Jaff and Drift at local and national level, but Gael was irreplaceable.

Dumfriesshire farmer Joe Johnstone of Garrieston, a man with the right words for the right time, paid this tribute to Gael on her death at 11½ years old in 1968:

> We'farmers and shepherds
> Who drove o'er the dale
> Mourn sadly thy passing
> Dear friendly old Gael.
>
> Off all the great dogs
> Whose tails ever curled
> You proved yourself top
> Of the whole canine world.
>
> No words can be said
> No words can be penned
> That would e'er do thee justice
> Old servant and friend.
>
> Twelve times you have heard
> The cuckoo's sweet call
> Twelve times you have witnessed
> The russet leaves fall.

You worked on the farm
And at the trials so game
But never yet knew
How great was your fame.

Today far and wide
Many pedigree claims
Your blood and your style
Flow strong in their veins.

Your trials are run
So peacefully sleep
Till the great final gather
When men are as sheep.

Though the curtain of time
Puts our minds in a fog
We'll love and remember thee
Wee collie dog.

While at a late age Gael managed to work honestly and purposefully for that supreme award there was another bitch who just failed to do so yet she too is a legend—David Shennan's white and tan Maid whom I first saw that same summer in which old Gael died.

David turned up at the Oxton trials at the foot of the Lammermuirs with a young smooth-clothed bitch which had been through several owners by then and which was not even registered by the International Sheep Dog Society. That run with the young Maid is still recalled today by David who went on in the next eight or nine years to win—by my reckoning—forty-four open championships with Maid. In addition there were victories at confined and holiday trials.

I last saw Maid in 1978, as spry a pensioner as there is, but inclined to stick close to the fire and leave the winter-garmented Carrick sheep rakes, which she had commanded and graced for so long, to others more agile.

A star worker for so long in the quiet world of sheepdog trials and a seven-day-week ungrudging tender of hill sheep and beef cattle near Girvan, she was content in semi-retirement. And conscious too that the fireside crack was many times about herself when visitors shared the hearth. Yet she turned out the next Saturday and won another trial at Neilston! And that was at 11½ years old and following a rally from arthritis which lost her most of two years in competitive work.

In her career I reckon she competed at well over 300 trials. She was a celebrity in the working shepherd and flockmaster's pastime of trialling and also an essential cog from morning to night in David Shennan's livestock operations at Knockgerran farm.

In many thousands of miles of Saturday trialling she even competed

134

at four events in one day taking many score of awards back to the rising sheep walks near Barr. She won the B.B.C. 'One Man and his Dog' champion of champions award; appeared in front of Royalty at exhibitions and had been painted and sculpted. But the big one—the International supreme championship—eluded the pair.

They were runners-up once. Maid represented Scotland four times at International level.

David Shennan once summed up her ability thus: "She's one of the hardiest tykes with cattle that I have about and that is the first essential here. If the dogs cannot get in a good day's work at home they will not be travelling the country with me."

Maid did both. Many early morning starts from Knockgerran meant a trip taking in several trials in the same day. In one trip David ran two dogs at the Great Glen trials near Fort William, motored down and repeated this at Kilmore, near Oban, headed for Killearn for another two droves and finished up at Dalmellington at night with two more spells of gathering sheep. Maid's contribution to this trip was a fourth at the Great Glen (she won it three times), a third at Kilmore, a fourth at Killearn and the championship at Dalmellington. She was not even tired.

In 1972 Maid gained eleven victories ranging from Newton Stewart to Monymusk and Kingussie. Behind all the awards again is the blue-blood of the working collie. Gaining registration in the ISDS stud book on merit through her early Oxton victory her breeding goes back through some of the noted hill dogs of J. M. Wilson including his Tweed, Moss, Whitehope Nap and Cap. There were four crosses of Whitehope's great Nap dog in her.

"You need something with some sting about it—you need a good rubbing of this Nap blood," David once told me. Also there as a great-grandmother is the bitch featured earlier in the chapter, Thomson McKnight's wise old Gael.

In her more elderly days in the late 1970's, David said Maid did not tire easily when she was working. "There is a lot of running in her and she does not spare herself any. I don't think I will ever have another like her. If I could get one at two years old just now like Maid I would think I was a lucky man. Her record speaks for itself."

There is another bitch I must mention for in my years covering the sheepdog trials scene she became one of my favourites for her pith, her character and her practical shepherding—William Cormack's prick-eared black and white June from the sheep and beef country near the Pentland Firth at Dunnet in Caithness.

I had visited the Cormack family's 300-acre farm away back in 1969 when I made a point of journeying north each winter to write of sheepdog men. But it was in 1973 in Dundee parkland that William Cormack became the first Caithness man to gain the Scottish Championship handling the then four year old smallish June, a collie which deserves a place in any

135

annals of the pastime.

June usually calls attention to herself at any trial for she still takes the 'stop' command on a pea whistle and when so many handlers were letting points spill left, right and centre at Dundee, little June shepherded handsomely to the championship. She was bred at Bonar Bridge by James Coghill from parents with Gilchrist's Spot blood—Coghill's Moss and June which were bred by Sandy McLay, East Calder. It was blood going back to Wallace's Loos, including that of Purdie's Roy and Tam 11, Templeton's Roy and Tom Wilson's Lassie.

So that year, as captain of the Scottish team, William Cormack had to travel the length of three countries—a 600-mile hurl—to take part in the centenary International at Bala in North Wales, only a whistle-length from where the pastime began. And she staggered the thousands watching the Friday's wonderful qualifying class work with the most brilliant practical shepherding session of the three days. And, alas, had nothing to show for it.

Completing his classic spell William perhaps asked just too much of the Scottish champion when it came to single out the last sheep and there was an indiscretion—in other words, she was alleged to have gripped a ewe. It was one of these slim chances which are there and vanish at the very instant of decision.

At home on the hill or field there would have been no going back. June just did her duty—and practically the impossible—in slicing out the ribboned ewe. In doing so, regrettably, she got that grip. What a sad sight to see the course director walk over to William as he left the ring and give him the information that he had been disqualified.

Rules are rules—I got into trouble from certain ISDS heirarchy by writing at the time that maybe the rules could do with a bit more flexibility—but this was just a dog getting something practical done and, let us be honest, her value at home—and that of all working dogs—is in the need sometimes to take such action if need be. There are home circumstances which can warrant it or you are going to look gey glaikit walking half a mile to bring down an obstinate bissom of a ewe.

William, happily, was back when the International again came to Bala in 1980 with a daughter of June and in fact the old maiden nearly made it herself and would have done so had she not missed a gate at the Scottish National that year.

There is one other bitch which stands out in my memory around 1975. She was a beast who did not, regrettably, have a long life but belonged to a good friend, Sandy McFern, now shepherding near Auchencairn, Castle Douglas.

He described his little Mist as 'jeest a flechlin o' a beast'. She was one of the jolliest, friendliest and most honest of collies. Mist was the most unlikeliest working sheepdog I have seen, rakish, small and inquisitive for no matter how the McFern family fed her she never put on weight or filled out.

At Moniaive sheepdog trials she found out that the catering tent provided excellent pies and she carried this knowledge to all the trials to which she was taken. I never yet spotted her at a trial without seeing her coming jauntily out of the tent wolfing a pie. She was as keen on her work too and when she died tragically early in her years it was a big loss to Sandy and to the trials world for she looked to me like being one of the most promising dogs of the decade. She might have become another of the legendaries.

CHARACTERS

Every trip and every day produces a worthy—the characters whose tasks or tales made daily traipses throughout the length and breadth of the land tolerable and fascinating. There was the water diviner, the farmer in the shadow of a power station who preferred the paraffin lamp, the gun-toting West Coast American range farmer whose collies wore deerskin boots, the shepherd who returned to horseback tending of sheep on his South Atlantic isle and the former shepherd who made fame and fortune with a capital F. These and many, many more.

An old whalebone let Edwin Taylor, the water diviner, see a new dimension in the land he walked. A noted British Friesian and Bluefaced Leicester breeder he could feel beyond the grass, dykes, fences and livestock to another world.

A twitch or a pull from the whalebone as he walked over hill ground or townside fields and he could tell from experience and self-gained knowledge that there was an underground stream so many feet wide possibly 90 ft underground carrying a given gallonage of water a day.

If he forgot to put the whalebone in his jacket pocket he would cut a Y-shaped hazel twig, the traditional trade tool of the water dowsers. Even if he could not find a hazel, thumbs would do, said Edwin, who has spent many hours finding new sources of water for farms. Successfully too, for when I met with him, he had never failed to find water when requested.

As old a craft as shepherding itself, dowsing is "just a nice hobby or pastime from which I get a lot of pleasure," said Edwin who was farming with his son Edwin jnr., 900 acres near Shotley Bridge in Co. Durham when I wrote a feature on him.

The dairy side of the farming set-up there had contributed to the dowsing aspect, for the two lengths of whalebone which are Edwin's principal tools, were fastened with a piece of milking machine rubber. At that time Edwin was a council member of the ancient British Society of Dowsers, who are known world-wide.

He had begun his divining pastime with pieces of fencing wire. "I began to get more and more confidence in what I could do as a dowser. I built up confidence by going round local farms getting to know their wells and finding that without exception, every well I saw had been found by a water diviner in some bygone period. I also followed springs. They would come out on to the surface and I would follow them back into the earth, measure their quantity, measure their depth and likewise in reverse, find underground streams and track them onto the surface.

"Having done this and proved beyond doubt that it was possible, I felt confident that I could go out and predict that I would find a supply of water for some needy person wherever he might be.

"You begin to see through a different pair of eyes. A field is not only covered with grass. You get to know that there are perhaps two underground streams. It puts a different pattern on the countryside.

"Getting hold of a stick is not the important thing. The important thing is knowing what the stick's reaction means when it pulls or comes down. You are a completely blind man before you give some measure of study to the method of dowsing and probably the types of strata in the area.

"Farming requirements, too, come into it and, in my sphere, this has been very useful and even possibly the whole crux of my success in understanding the needs of farmers in their requirements for water supplies. An awful lot of study has to go into the role."

The object, added Edwin, was to find sufficient water at the least depth possible. The ability to do this on a hill farm, for a local authority, private body or individual householder, can save a mighty expensive drilling operation.

While many diviners hold their rods with the Y-end extended, Edwin walks his ground in search of water mostly with the closed or forked end facing his chest. "If you want to get results, it has to be a firm hold of the rods or whatever you are using. In other words, you have to resist it."

He regularly gets called to hill farms and finds the tenants or owners surprised when he asks them: "Where would you like to find water?"

"That is the best way to start. For instance if you want an electric immersible pump put down a hole you want to be as near power as possible. Go to the place where the farmer wants water and you will soon feel where the nearest point is. Then you will not be long in finding it. You will find the course of the water at right angles, then cross it. Then you will not have too much bother deciding the width of the stream. The width will tell you the quantity of water running. Proceed from there until you come to the first waveband, holding the rod firmly.

"The distance in feet from the edge of the underground stream to the point where this wave is felt is equivalent to the depth where the water will be found.

"All you have to do is build up your confidence by going round and verifying your reactions," said Edwin. He has met many sceptics. "But when I said 'You have a try' you should have seen the expressions on their faces when they found a reaction with the rods."

In bygone days, the local diviner, said Edwin, was a very important personality in the country districts. He added that all the wells he now finds were originally located by dowsers. "Usually they're spot-on although occasionally you may get one that is on the side of a stream, that is, on the first of the wavebands."

Edwin's hobby has taken him to many areas in the North of England and into Scotland. He even found a supply for a sizeable community in Yorkshire and geologists following up his advice found water within one foot of his predictions.

Four lords and a duke called him in to help track a supply. He has helped out golf clubs, estate owners. Government departments, the Ministry of Agriculture and the National Trust.

"It has become more and more evident that something should be done by the people with the ability to go out and find water. They are not being put to their proper use. It is being proved more and more every day that the water diviner is a useful person. I am sure there was an age when he was really recognised and that day might very well return," said Edwin.

There will be few, however, who will return to the old days of the paraffin lamps. But one farmer I called on in 1969 was still using them—less than a field's length from the towers of one of Britain's nuclear power stations.

It was round about Burns day when I visited Norman Graham Barnett at the sixty-five-acre Blackhills farm, in my own calf country between the village of Creca and Annan in Dumfriesshire and came across the wistful reminder of the quieter days of bygone times.

Although the paraffin lamp was still the sole means of light at that time in the spotless homestead, Norman had given in to acquiring some machinery on the mixed farm—a tractor and a combine harvester. "Mind you, I don't like to see these things or the other modern machinery. I liked the old slow pace of life we used to have. I have old-fashioned tastes," he told me.

There were then two lines of electricity poles crossing the powerless farm. "There is something very romantic about the paraffin lamps," said Norman who was celebrating his silver wedding the next month and had lived all his married life at Blackhills. He and his wife were both keen readers and found the lamps caused less eye-strain.

Norman is a descendant of Dr Moore, a great friend of Burns and admits a lot of his old fashioned tastes have been instilled through his devotion to the Bard. "On the things he had held up as virtues I have gone all the way with him."

He often delved into the past. Much in demand as a speaker at all types of functions, he once gave a talk on that great drover John Cameron. The son of a crofter, Cameron made his first journey south wearing footless stockings and on one later occasion was said to have ridden more than 200 miles in under two days on a droving.

Norman first heard of Cameron from a descendant of the drover who came over from New Zealand during the last war. But it is back to Burns and if there is one thing Norman Barnett relishes—and so do his audiences—it is 'Tam o' Shanter' with perhaps 'Holy Willie's Prayer'

140

coming next.

What residents in an Annan hotel would have said had they come along the corridor one Burns night and seen the farmer emerging from a bedroom in a 'nicht-sark' and a long red bonnet, carrying a big Bible and a half-gallon container of whisky as he went to make his appearance as Holy Willie at a Burns supper can only be imagined.

Norman has read every published biography on Burns and most of the other works. He has even proposed the Immortal Memory in verse himself.

Somebody else doing something unusual—at least to we traditionalists in Scotland—was a character who arrived at our house one night and regaled us with his talk of Border collies with deerskin boots taking yelled orders from hat-waving nomadic Basque herders in coyote-infested sheep mountains on the west coast of America.

Range farmer Dick Harvard from Lebanon, Oregon was in Scotland to seek "good everyday" dogs for his shepherds who work on thousand-strong bands of Rambouillet ewes which follow the snowline to 10,000 ft in the Cascade mountain range of Oregon.

Over the years our home became a mini United Nations with scores of travellers from foreign countries just calling to 'talk dog.' Dick Harvard was one of the most colourful. He had been a herder himself and at the time of his visit owned some 8,000 acres and leased another 42,000 linked by stock trail in the Oschbosh mountains, part of the Cascade range producing killing lambs from Suffolk x Hampshire tups—'bucks' as he called them.

For one always keen to hear of sheep management elsewhere, Dick's story of life with his herders provided a fascinating glimpse of an entirely different way of life. His sheep rotate-graze the desert in the winter and early spring and then follow the melting snow to higher places. They are always threatened, no matter the vigilance of the herders, by a vast predator menace including mountain lions, eagles, bobcats and the coyote.

"The coyote is the one which really raises the thunder," said Dick. "He can live in any environment. He can slip right in among a bunch of sheep and take a lamb clean as anything, you bet. They make a clean kill. They are not messy killers."

This can sometimes mean a fair mortality amongst his stock which are tended by immigrant shepherds from the Basque country in Spain and from Peru. They stay with the sheep all the year round, herding from their 'camps' which are just mobile homes. In the summer, on the mountains, they use tents and each man usually looks after a thousand ewes, moving his camp weekly.

"When they start the season," Dick told me "they set up their camp. Then they start the sheep grazing away from it and they feed until they bed-up or are full. Around two or three o'clock the herder feeds them back in the direction of the camp and by dusk they have gone the full

141

distance back. Every day the herder takes them out in a different direction—we call it the wagon-wheel system—and after seven days he moves to another area.

As spring turns to summer the herders move further from the desert into the foothills and onto higher ground above the timber line following the melting snow. Sometimes the men go on horseback.

Bells on the collar of about every tenth ewe means that the herder can be wakened by the noise during the night if the sheep try to move away or if they are threatened by predators.

There is also a simple way of cutting out weaker sheep, subsequently maintaining a hardy stock. "When we are moving the sheep these distances to a complete new range we let them cull themselves. The weak ones which cannot keep up are just left behind. It is the only way we can keep a good strong band of ewes. People say it is cruel, but if you had to go back every night to gather these tailers it would be terrible and would get worse and worse. After the third day we don't get these problems."

Life can be hard on the collies too. Dick usually furnishes each herder with dogs if they do not already have them. At the time of his trip to Scotland he had around fifteen Border Collies at home with more to join them following his visit.

"Their main task is to keep strays with the main bunch for these herders, to move them and keep them under control. We would be lost without the Border Collie. We probably do not move sheep as much as in Scotland. We are keen on letting them feed and the dogs keep the bands from spreading out.

"We have to make boots to have ready in case there is heavy snow. This can get crusted with the frost and become as sharp as knives."

The boots are made from deerskin with gaps for the dog's nails and run some five or six inches up the legs. They are put on daily by the herders who do not normally use whistle commands but give orders to their collies by yelling or waving their hats.

I got to know another horseback shepherd, Galloway-born Tom McGhie who with his Scots-bred collies now tends Polwarth sheep on an 80,000-acre spread on the windswept, treeless Falkland Islands in the South Atlantic.

We had corresponded for some time before Tom and his family arrived back in this country in the middle '70's. He shepherded at Castlefairn, Moniaive, but the lure of the Falklands and its less materialistic life drew him back and the family returned in 1977 to Roy Cove in the West Falkland Islands.

Tom's wife Moira could hardly wait to get back to her peat cooker, penguin egg breakfast, the chance of Christmas Day on the beach and making jam from the fruit of the didle-dee plant. Their three children, then aged from five to fifteen, were also eager to return to their Swedish type house on the sheep station where Tom had shepherded fine-wooled sheep for nine years from 1965 to 1974.

Tom was turning his back once more on Scottish sheep work to return to the same job, later to be joined after quarantine by the three collies which shared his herding work at Castlefairn. The McGhies had missed too much many of the simple but satisfying aspects of life on their station some thirteen miles from the main settlement on the roadless island where they would have camps of eight-year-old wethers to tend, have sides of beef hanging outside in the winter and cruel turkey vultures to watch out for at lambing time.

The McGhies station stocked some 20,000 Polwarth sheep to help boost the island's main industry—wool. The unit is split into several camps which are sometimes 'fields' as big as 700 acres. Hence the need of horses to get round the stock. There were twenty-two horses on the land to which Tom was eagerly returning, mostly of Arab and Welsh Cob blood.

Some of the wethers run on mountain camps up to 1,800 ft and these are shepherded about three times a year. The ewes start to lamb in September and shearing time is in February.

The McGhies home—there are six bedrooms, bathroom, sitting room, kitchen, pantry and back-kitchen with a diesel generator—is about 100 miles from Port Stanley in the West Falklands, probably the most southerly town in the world and with around 1,000 people at that time. Parallel streets run up from the shore and this is the only area where there are roads, though Land Rovers can easily traverse the islands tracks.

The other mode of travel is by Government floatplanes which come into the bay beside the McGhies home twice a week. The six-seater planes are used by the doctor, teachers and for delivering mail and messages. By a radio telephone link, island settlers can contact stores to order any goods and if these are not breakable they are sometimes dropped overhead the stations out of the planes.

The station also had its own store selling a range of items from clothing to kitchen needs, beers and spirits. But Moira always kept a bulk supply of flour, sugar etc. and was again planning to bake her own bread using the peat fired Raeburn cooker. Employees on the station are paid by the yard to cut peat for themselves.

All the stations have space for dance floors. They come in handy at weddings for if an announcement is made over the island radio about a forthcoming wedding that means everyone is invited. Teachers go the rounds staying two weeks with families who have children of school age.

Each station also takes its part in the rota of celebrations which follows the end of the clipping season. There is a week of sports, sheepdog trials, steer-riding competitions, gymkhanas and dancing every night—at a different station each year.

From the mighty acreages of these camps and stations in Oregon and the Falklands to four acres on Edinburgh's southerly boundaries is a vast jump, but a flock of twelve sheep on that tiny strip ensures the continual successes of another of the sheepdog world's most noted personalities—Dick Fortune, a character who has shepherded in the quiet Scottish glens, mustered in the vast Mackenzie country of New Zealand for sixteen shillings a day, made up to £1,000 for showyard demonstrations with sheepdogs and gained some of the highest honours in the trials world.

Nowadays, he regularly works his collies not far from where he started life as a shepherd boy with the noted Jeffrey family at Little Spot in East Lothian. Their Border Leicester, Oxford and Hill Cheviot stock were renowned in the early 1930's.

His knowledge of sheep expanded rapidly and within five years he had set up a British shearing record with the old-fashioned hand clippers. At Hangingshaw farm he clipped 170 rough Half-Bred ewes in one day. That includes catching the ewes and rolling the fleeces in a pen against a dyke and he still has the newspaper story to prove it.

It was not long after that, when he was making around £2 a week in 1935—six shillings a score was the shearing pay as Dick travelled round work and sheepdog trials in Scotland on a motorbike with a sidecar box for his dogs—that Dick replied to an advertisement seeking someone to train sheepdogs in New Zealand for James Lilico of Lochiel, Southland.

Dick landed the job and his fare was paid with the promise of £2 a week plus food and keep. He took two collies with him—George Lauder's Mist and the English-bred Pat at a freight cost of £7 a head.

James Lilico had two noted stud dogs when Dick arrived. They were Cheviot Toss and Hayton's Kep. Lilico was at that time the biggest importer of Border Collies to New Zealand.

Dick eventually left to manage a sheep run in Canterbury and then had a season at high Mesopotamia Station up the Rakaia Gorge. "Seven of us were mustering that country which then had 20,000 Merino sheep," said Dick who used old Mist for heading work and commanded four Huntaway dogs.

From there the Scot got his own mixed wheat and sheep farm of some 350 acres in Level Valley, Timaru. He also leased 2,000 acres twenty miles away.

Five years after he left the UK shores, Dick returned on a purchasing visit for dogs and sailed back with seven collies which were to help him establish himself as a maestro working a team. By then he had already started to earn trials prizes, for soon after his original arrival he ran Mist at the Invercargill Royal Show and won it. But during the later war years he concentrated on giving exhibitions and raised a lot of money for the war effort. He reckons to be the first man in that part of the world to give exhibitions with such a large number of workers.

His first exhibition was in 1939 at the Dunedin Show with five collies but later he was to thrill audiences with up to eight dogs. One of his most skilled partners was the smooth-coated Meg known in New Zealand and Australia as Margaret Rose. Bought from Andrew Carruthers of Yetholm,

144

she went out in 1947 and was "one of the best collies ever to cross the equator," says Dick. "She won nine successive firsts in nine starts in New Zealand."

He thought nearly as much of Mirk, taken out in the early fifties from Tom Watson, Scottish handler of International repute. Mirk ran two 99-point trials in New Zealand. Another good one before that was Vic, a son of Gilchrist's old Spot to whom a great number of prominent dogs in Scotland today can be traced back.

Dick competed in New Zealand championships and the highest placing he got was a fourth with Mirk. But on the other side of the Tasman he once gained the Queensland championship. It was during one of several exhibitions given on trips to Australia which stemmed from Aussies seeing his work in New Zealand.

One series of nine exhibitions—some under floodlight—at the Sydney Show earned him £1,000. He demonstrated twice at the Melbourne, Brisbane and Sydney Royal Shows. At that time his kennel back near Timaru had the biggest number of imported sheepdogs in New Zealand, says Dick, and he reckoned he had sold about 120 annually there and in Australia. In all this he thinks he took at least 100 dogs to New Zealand over a twenty-year period.

Dick sold off his New Zealand farming interests in 1956 and returned to the Scottish borderland where he acquired a farm near Selkirk. He sold this and purchased one south of the border near Chester before retiring from farming in 1961 and settling in Edinburgh.

These twelve Blackface ewes on his four acres just opposite the ski-slope on the Biggar road are far removed from Mackenzie sheep counts but they have kept his collies in trim and Dick has consistently been high in Scottish trials placings in recent years.

After trialling for about forty-five years he gained one of Scotland's major national championships, in 1975, the Farmers event with Jill. Nowadays with his two collies he will be picking up at least 100 prizes a year on the Scottish circuit.

THE OLD SCHOOL

Memories of yesterday come into sharper focus as life etches its progress deeper on a countryman's features. Or is it nowadays that life's happenings are sometimes not worth pigeon-holing in the mind?

Tapes, computers and micro-films will spew out the essentials of the recent decades. A pity, for technology will not be able to retell the past so vividly as the likes of Andrew Renwick, Willie Goodfellow, Willie Dunn, Hugh Cameron and dozens of others I have listened to at their ingles.

Where Andrew Renwick got his first whiff of farming they have now housed thousands of folk on his former soor milk farm. There is crowded habitation too on the former 130-acre Edinburgh farm where he used to single turnips and stook wheat and oats for the capital's many permanently-housed dairy herds.

The causey stanes have long gone from the streets where he carted straw bunches and chaff bags to dealers, coachmen, vanmen and merchants and where he was regularly on haulage of dung back to the farm from the city dairies—with the occasional five shilling fine to pay when some dropped off the back of his cart.

Five bob was five bob in these days just at the turn of the century when Andrew had a few years of suburban farming within Edinburgh's boundary—one of several growers of turnips, ryegrass, wheat and oats to provide for the cattle stalled within the city, cattle which were milked until they gave no more.

Andrew was in his ninetieth year when I met him in 1976. He had an easy memory for these days and even times before that on his grandmother's farm in Maryhill, Glasgow. At the time I called he had been retired for about twenty-two years following some forty-five years tenancy of farms near Haddington and Bonnyrigg. He had a memory too for the likes of Tom Dickson, Jamie Scott, Sandy Millar, Tom Gilholm and the other legendary men of sheepdogdom, each worth many a story. (There was Tom Dickson's famed collie, Foozle, for instance, which bolted after a rabbit on a critical part of a sheepdog trial, earthed it in a burrow, returned to his course and gained a prize.)

Andrew's grandmother had a farm at Maryhill where he spent his first seventeen years. She had forty cows and sold the buttermilk from the 'soor milk cairt' in the north side of the city along such thoroughfares as Garscube Road and Maryhill Road. Much of it went to grocers but it also entailed lads—Andrew among them—hurtling up and down the closes and stairheads selling to housewives in what was a competitive business between various dairy firms.

Andrew left Glasgow in 1903 to work on his father's rented farm at East Pilton inside Edinburgh's boundary, one of the units providing feed for the city's dairy herds.

"Nearly all the milk was produced inside the city," said Andrew. "There were dairies by the score in the Stockbridge and Leith areas. Most of them had forty cows although there were some big ones in Leith with about 100 milkers.

"Mostly at East Pilton we were growing early turnips and Italian ryegrass for the dairymen. The ryegrass was sold by auction in half-acre plots. The land at East Pilton was measured off with ash tracks every 200 yards. There were two or three farms on the outskirts of the town laid off like that. I remember Olivers, the auctioneers, selling the ryegrass from six farms in the one night. They hired two horse traps for driving some of their customers around. Father was getting about £23-£24 an acre for ryegrass and £27-£28 for yellow turnips.

"The Italian ryegrass was about three feet long at the time of the sale. Some dairymen who came to the sale brought a scythe, cut a load and took it home that night. All their cattle were inside most of the time and mostly of the English Shorthorn breed. At one time there was a lot of Dutch cattle coming into Leith but in 1892 these importations stopped."

After the harvest Andrew delivered bunches of straw to shops, coachmen, vanmen and grocers for four years. "We bagged the chaff off the grain and sold to merchants. Most of it went into chaff beds until the Town Council made this illegal."

Another of his chores in the winter time when ploughing was done, was to cart out dung from the town dairies and spread it on the land. There were horse trams and even cable cars during some of his horse-and-cart journeys into the city over the cobbles and the jogging over these stones could lead sometimes to that five shilling fine if dung was dropped on the street.

When he left suburban farming in 1907 Andrew took tenancy of the arable unit of the Byres, two miles north of Haddington and stayed for thirty-two years before going to Dalhousie Chesters farm at Bonnyrigg. He retired from there to his home in Dalkeith.

A purchase of eighty Blackface ewes at a Haddington sale from Sandy Swanston who was a noted sheepdog trials official, first gave Andrew an interest in trials and for many years he followed the events and the characters.

Somebody who got into the sheepdog trials company of old in a different manner—with the help of a funeral—was Willie Dunn. He had missed the bus over the hill from Moniaive to Dalry on the exposed Dumfriesshire-Galloway boundary when heading for his first open trial

147

with a blue merle collie.

Willie, a former award-winning catch-as-catch-can wrestler from the Ochils who took that blue dog and an old belt-driven Rudge motor-bike combination to a job beside the River Nith, was shepherd then at the Crichton Royal Mental Institute on the edge of Dumfries.

"It was a snowy day in October," he told me at his home at Carsebreck, near Blackford, Perthshire, when recalling that Dalry event in 1927. "I had got the bus from Dumfries to Moniaive alright but the bus over to Dalry had gone when I got there. Somebody shouted to me that there was a funeral party going some of the way and I might get a lift with them. In fact I got about halfway with that party and walked the remainder."

Because of weather conditions at the trial, Willie just stood in a byre and did not see anyone else compete before his time came to trial with the blue merle dog which was named Marle. He came right back to the byre after completing the course. It was his first ever trial. "Then at night I went down to get the result. I was seventh. I thought I had done well for in front of me were such worthies as Sandy Millar, Jim Wilson and Tom Dickson."

Marle, had come into his hands as a pup from George Gilholm of Aberlady who was to play a big part in his trials career. Willie was in his eighty-first year when I called at his Blackford home, a few years before his death. He was in the Scottish team several times and his collies were all descended from Gilholm's Fan and Phil which were full sisters.

A native of Sauchie in Clackmannanshire, Willie used to travel every Sunday to George Gilholm's farm "to be amongst collies." A few years later for a fiver, he acquired two sheepdogs, Myrtle and Winnie from George and got his name into the record books with their off-spring, which included, Dusk and Winnie. They were at the front of the Shepherd's class at the Scottish National trials of 1935 in Helensburgh and the International shepherds class of the same year at Blackpool. By this time Willie was manager at Capenoch, near Thornhill, Dumfriesshire.

The 1935 victory at Helensburgh was the only time Willie ran as a shepherd at the National, for the next year he had taken tenancy of Duallin farm at Lawers in Perthshire and was in the Farmers' section where he finished second with Dusk, a daughter of John Murray's Drift.

Another Willie, who could enthrall his listeners, was Willie Goodfellow who told of a life shepherding and farming on fell and beside forest. Some of his memorable early days were in Irthing Vale just over the Border in Cumbria and by the two homesteads of Redsike and Paddaburn. Word has it that the Goodfellows never allowed the Redsike peat fire to go out for 200 years.

It was as a fourteen-year-old that Willie first took to a herding at Moscow farm, Gilsland on "really old-fashioned, heavy-skinned sheep." That was round about 1912.

"In my young days when you went to help gather sheep, every man had a good hill dog—dogs with brains. Not many of them were registered. These dogs got more time to mature. They were left to do things their own way and they were not dictated to as they are nowadays," said Willie during a fireside chat in 1971. "They could be sent away to gather sheep and you did not bother any more about them. These people could leave a dog with a cut of sheep and get away down to the pen, get on with the work and the dogs were still lying with the sheep.

"The old-fashioned men who used to run dogs allowed them time to think and the dogs could get time to balance. A lot of them have no balance nowadays—they are just going to commands."

As a young shepherd Willie moved to Dudleys, near Otterburn for South Country Cheviot breeder, George Murray. He took Glen with him, the first collie he had owned, one of the last of his father's breeding. Its grandfather was one of the blue-grey dogs off the Bewcastle area.

"We had an awful bad snowstorm in March and I always say I would not have got home but for that dog. It came on so quick the time we were out on the fell. The wind just rose. Coming from the North-East, it was like a train roaring. I was blinded by the snow, but Glen kept turning back and coming in front of me and he guided me back to the gate that took us to the park field beside the house."

After the war and now married, he shepherded at The Green, some ten miles north of Wark village, right on the hills. That back-end he got a six month old bitch Fan from a young shepherd for fifty shillings. "I'll never forget that bitch," said Willie enthusing over the way she once took part in a three-day drove over the fell into Bewcastle area taking Cheviots and Blackfaces to Longtown. "She certainly knew something at the end of that trek. She used to slide away down the side of the sheep at all the junctions and stop them from going the wrong way. We walked all the way back that night through the snow. It was a good moonlit night and it was quiet but there was a hard frost. It was a great experience for the bitch too, for by then she was only nine months old. She was a grand beast—one of the best I ever had on the hill."

It was that Fan bitch which accompanied Willie on his first-ever foray to a sheepdog trial. He had then moved from Wark and was near Bardon Mill in charge of a big sheep stock so he entered the nearby Haltwhistle event. "I was pleased to get off the field I can tell you," said Willie. "Fan did everything I asked her, but we did not get any prizes. The same year I went to Allendale and was fourth with her. I also won the special prize at Hexham trials—a pair of boots."

At one time Willie had his own farm, 3,400 acres of which were destined for the Kershope Forest, then he got tenancy of Hole o' Lyne where he stayed until 1948. It was when he returned to the Newcastleton area of Roxburghshire that he won the Scottish National Sheepdog Trials championship at Kelso in 1958 with Laddie. The year before, Laddie had won nine cups, and prior to that, Willie had gained team places in 1953 with Queen, 1955 with Roy and 1956 with Laddie.

A dog is still valued these days if you can say he is of the Goodfellow's Laddie line. Willie was a regular attender at trials though walking on two artificial limbs. He died in the Autumn of 1980. His kind do not come to a halt on retirement.

It was the same with Hugh Cameron who, fit and young at seventy-two belted out the 'Herds Wallop' on the fiddle when I met him in 1972. Maybe the homely living room of a Sutherland croft was not the place you would expect to hear it. I always believed it to be a jig for the south hill people.

But Hugh Cameron still had a gleg finger, a good ear and a solid boot to mark time. One wishes there was more time and less tarmacadam to hear other strains on a winter's afternoon. There are too few abodes now where the fiddle—once in nearly every 'herding homestead—gets an airing. (They are for playing lads. They are for playing—and passing on to the next generation. Not for flogging to the antique dealers).

The one I heard on the Sutherland croft had been tuned in many an airt of our countryside. Hugh Cameron would likely be playing the 'Herd's Wallop' many a year before as the sheep men of Carrick and Galloway stepped it out around Barr dances. It has also gone into the Invernesshire fastness of the Locheil countryside which stretches to Morar; and to the Cheviot and black cattle ground of Eriboll where the tenant over the dyke is Neptune.

Hugh, crofting fourteen acres at Torroble, above Lairg, with added common grazing rights, was a retailer of stories and experiences. Such a life which ranged from the rugged burnheads of Galloway to Renfrewshire, Perthshire and the north-west vastness meant time for thinking of collies, sheep and men. His role as a shepherd, head shepherd and estate manager, meant a boot on each foot and a balanced view of the part of trial dogs. Of these he had much experience, highlighted by winning the Shepherds Championship at the 1950 Scottish National trials with the tan-undercoated Queen.

"I never put a dog first," Hugh told me. "I have been in managerial posts most of the time and once had a man who put his dogs first. He wasn't much use to me. I have always been very keen on a good dog but at the same time I have entered for many a trial and, when I found work was not going to allow me to go to the trial, I did not go and got on with the work.

"There is many a man who objects to his shepherd going to trials. If a man finds himself in that position he should look after the bread and butter. I do not mean he should give up trials. But he could shift to another place."

Hugh had retained the same bloodlines in his collies away back to 1924 with his own Queen blood and the strain which goes back to Troneyhill Kep. These Cameron collies had worked in various parts of our land. A

150

son of Lochaber from a family who had been shepherds for generations, originating from Ardnamurchan, he started his 'herding career at Flanders Moss between Stirling and Aberfoyle. This was on a three-mile wide moss which was split by man-made ditches four yards wide and ten feet deep "and with the biggest adders in the whole of Scotland."

If a sheep was in trouble perhaps only a short distance away he might have to walk 300 yards to get across a plank over one of the ditches. Hugh discovered later they had been made as part of a reclamation scheme in the 17th century.

He had spells on the Merrick range of hills in Galloway, at Kilbirnie and in the Spean Bridge airt before returning to Ayrshire and then heading back north to Locheil Estates to take charge of 60,000 acres at the head of Loch Arkaig. His family would be the last to dwell at Glendessary, an hour's trip up the loch-side where Hugh was in charge of the area running to Loch Morar where shepherds sometimes had to travel by boat. The size of the next herding at Eriboll Estates meant he had little time for trials.

The collie Queen, which put Hugh's name in the record books with that Shepherds title in 1950, was a black and tan prick-eared bitch. She was bred by Robert Burns of Braco who later went to New Zealand, by his Ben dog, a son of N. Fortune's Watt and J. J. Scott's Fan. One of the descendants of Queen was David McTeir's Mirk, another champion.

Some of Hugh's early collies travelled on two wheels. "I used to take a dog on the front of my motor bike. I have seen me travelling miles and miles like that—they sat on the tank with their forefeet on the handlebars.

"I have seen a devil of a lot of good dogs. There was one outstanding run in my mind and I never saw the likes of it again. It was when Jim Wilson went to the post at Edinburgh around 1956 and ran Glen. He just cracked his fingers and the dog went round the sheep and stopped at 12 o'clock. He came away with the sheep himself, right through the gates and up to Jim's feet. Jim stood there and never opened his mouth. I never saw a dog that could do that without a word of command and have a straighter course. This is where a lot of folk do not make the best of things. They do not let things alone when they might come off."

Hugh would not have recognised his former herding ground near the Merrick if he had returned to it in the late 1970's. There will be no more lambings there and life has undergone another vast change around that hill and the Gaelic-sounding rigs and lochans of the high land which takes Galloway into Carrick.

"It is wild, rough country," said David Murdoch, eighty years old when I met him and off his sheep hefts at Water of Minnoch simply because the sheep had gone. The trees had come, as they came to Drumjohn, Bargrennan where he had started his lambing career at twelve years of age. He went to Taryfessock for his first full-time job. "There used to be three 'herds at Taryfessock, now there are trees," he said.

151

David, whose six sons became shepherds, could recall between forty and fifty shepherds in that district. Forestry cleared them nearly 100 per cent. There are no more tales to be told of the sheep, men, dogs, families, storms and events in that once-famed sheep land.

HIGHLAND HEROES

The Highlanders enjoy their work. From the high mountain pads of the west to the flagstone boundaries of Caithness there are plenty of sheep and folk skilled in doglore who recall cherished days and memorable happenings.

There is told in the croftlands, the story of a respected shepherd who gave over sixty years service to his laird. In that time he had hardly ventured from his cottage home or the heaths and the sheep with which he daily communed.

Only perhaps once or twice a year did he venture to Fort William or Oban from the fastness of the west coast for the sales. To his embarrassment, the laird organised a presentation dinner for him and invited the gentry and the shepherds to pay tribute to the shepherd's sixty-five years of service. They came from Knoydart, from Morven, from Ardnamurchan, from Strontian and from further afield to the ceilidh.

Unused to such socialising the old shepherd sat in a fusion of glumness and shyness as the evening wore on and all but vanished from his seat when His Lordship, the laird, took to his feet to extol the virtues of his great servant, his value and his long service. The embarrassment became even more acute when, after being presented with a comfortable armchair as a gift, the 'herd realised he had to thank the assembled village hall audience for the present and the hospitality.

There was no way out for a soul, who, though well into his 70's, would rather have been among the Blackfaces, the rocks and the high pastures he knew well and who had never spoken a word at a public gathering before.

He faltered to his feet to give his thanks: "My . . . your Lordsh . . . . your High . . . er . . . . your Grace, it is . . . . er . . . . ladies and gent . . . your worship . . . . I am not used . . . . this is not a . . . . I have to apolog . . . . er . . . . lairdship . . . . er my good friends, unaccustomed as . . . . this is an . . . . . er . . . . embarras . . . . I just don't know how to beg . . . . . er MAUN SHE'S BLASHY WATHER FUR THE LAMBIN."

Yes, the Highlanders enjoy their work. I discovered a homely legend in the neat china cups once when calling at a Badenoch homestead. It meant a talk about Ness—the collie once destined to go abroad as a gift but which stayed at home and gained a place in the record books when herding Welsh sheep for the first lady to compete in an International Sheep Dog Trial.

153

The cups also told of wise old Swan, the rough-coated bitch which could even recognise her master's name when it was announced over loudspeakers. They related too, the doings of the white-headed Rye, of Meg, Tess and Queen, much of whose blood went right back to the beginnings of collie myth.

The tea cups pictured an interesting part of that history, recognising the chapter played by Annie McCormack, who first ran a collie at a trial in 1934 in her native Highland countryside and capped her career with that International appearance in 1962 with the black, white and tan Ness.

The collies Mrs McCormack ran over a fair span of years are faithfully reproduced and remembered in lifelike hand-painted China cups. A half-set pictures several of her better-known dogs and a whole set is devoted to Swan, "the best one I ever had."

"It was the best time of my life," said Mrs McCormack recalling the years when she travelled around a good number of trials. "But I never wanted to start again once I stopped.

"It never worried me being one of the only lady competitors. In fact the only worrying thing was having reporters coming up just when I was ready to go on to the course. 'What do you do'? Why do you like trials'? They asked all the stupid questions under the sun."

They pestered her on that visit as a Scottish team member to the hill outrun at the Beaumaris International in 1962 in Wales. Mrs McCormack had gained her team cap by coming fifth in the Farmers' Class—her Ness getting the same points as a collie which five years later was to win the supreme title, Thomson McKnight's Gael.

"Ness did not like flanking on the 'away to me' side," recalled Mrs McCormack in 1972. "I did a silly thing that day at the International. She was coming straight after a good outrun. I don't know what made me do it, but I stopped her. After that, she took the huff and would not take the 'away to me' flank." So the pair did not get through the qualifying round for the supreme championship running.

In a way Ness was lucky to be at the International. Off Watt Little's Cap and out of Mrs McCormack's own Swan, she was destined as a gift for Watt to take when he left to live in Canada. But she never went and was instead trained by the late Eck Storey from whom Mrs McCormack bought her back. And she went on to win Braco and Balvraid trials during her career.

On my visit in 1972 Mrs McCormack still had a collie going back to her internationalist Ness. But her trial visits then were more or less limited to time-keeping at the Laggan event.

It is not far from where she first commanded working sheepdogs on her father's farm at Nuide, Kingussie when she was still at school and from where she won the Farmers' Cup with Tess at Kingussie in 1936, her first success.

"We had about 2,000 sheep on my father's place. I was always at work on the sheep and when I left school I had a hirsel to myself. I had to put them up the hill at nights and they were always on the arable land during the day. They do not use that system so much nowadays.

"I was always keen on trial dogs. We used to drove the lambs in these days to the sales and they were just separated out on the hill. They don't do that now—they are just jammed on a haulage float. We had to walk three or four miles to Kingussie with lambs or put them on the train to Perth. These dogs were good on the road and watched all the holes in the fences to make sure the sheep did not bolt through."

The first open trial Mrs McCormack won was the Kingussie event in 1949 which she led with the silver-eyed black and mottled Meg, a dog bred by a roadman. One of the bitches she sent to New Zealand was Fan, the mother of the big-hearted Swan, Scotland's driving champion at the Scottish National in 1958. "She was a terribly wise dog. She knew when the loudspeaker said 'Mrs McCormack get ready.' "

Fan went back to Sandy Millar's Drift blood and was out of Mrs McCormack's own Winnie which can be traced back to No. 7 in the International Sheep Dog Society stud book—Adam Telfer's Moss.

The white-collared Swan was off Wattie Little's Roy and possibly had her best year in 1956. Her wins included a double at Thornton and victories at Watten, Falkland, Kingussie, Skye and also a much-remembered runners-up placing at Stirling, half a point behind the noted John Johnstone's Mirk.

These were good days. There was another day, perhaps, not so good. Sheep broke away during a trial at Cawder close by a farm steading. "I finished up in a pig sty with one sheep. I had to go in after her," recollected Mrs McCormack.

That would be a rare sight. So too would the chance of seeing a drove of 600 hoggs on the road from that same Kingussie countryside going through Nairn. Such is progress, however, with its axing of railway lines and rising haulage costs, that ere another fifty years we may have turned full cycle and gone back to droving.

So it might pay some of the youngsters to learn again—or find before they are lost—the old trekking pads, and set themselves up in business. And if they want to know the best land crossing from Kingussie to Nairn, then, as they say north of the Highland line "go you" to Donald MacLeod.

Donald is now firmly established at the other side of Struie and I can think of no more companionable character for a fireside crack than this crofter from a run of heather land above Bonar Bridge.

He can remember and tell vividly of those earlier days down Kingussie way. Life for the young 'herd then was to drive the hoggs over to Nairn in October—"that's the time you needed a hardy dog with you, one that could yank them up"—bring them back on the first of April, get in a lambing and then go ghillieing until October came round again.

The ghillie work was mostly in hauling back stags on horses for shooting tenants.

Collies were to become a bigger part in the life of Donald MacLeod. After a spell herding near Aviemore he spent twelve memorable years as collie trainer for the late Mr C. B. MacPherson of Balavil, one of the renowned sheepdog men of the north and described by Donald as one of the most extraordinary men he has ever met. He had always fifteen or twenty collies in his kennels, and callers from all over the world.

Among the collies which came to stay at Balavil was J. M. Wilson's Jim "along with Whitehope Cap one of the greatest dogs I ever saw," says Donald who was to become a great friend of Mr Wilson. It was from Mr MacPherson that Donald gained many hints. One was to take towels with him to sheepdog trials and dry off the collies if they had to run in wet conditions.

When Donald went to a war-time herding at Arisaig a pup was to emerge which became one of the backbone breeders of the day. Donald had with him at the time Joe, a son of Wilson's Cap, out of Tom Brotherstone's Tib and Gyp, the latter by Wilson's Jim, out of Brotherstone's good breeding bitch Beat. Mated, they left the black and white rough-coated Garry, a collie which went on to win the Scottish and International Shepherds championships and represented Scotland seven times. There is pride among dogmen when they can say their collie goes back to MacLeod's Garry—I have heard it many a time.

Garry won his first trial on his debut at Dalmally. War held back competitions but in 1946 in Donald's first entry at a National event, Garry took the premier shepherd's placing and did the same at the International. Next year he was second in the National and led the Qualifying round.

"There was never another like Garry. He was a natural good dog," said Donald. He left his mark on prizelists all over the country. In his last trials outrun at twelve years old he won Glendevon. He also left progeny which made their mark. There was the big bare-skinned Coon, a son of Garry out of Nan, a bitch Donald got from Jim Holmes and off this breeder's Jaff and Nell. When a year old and on his first outing he won Bonar Bridge trials after Donald moved up to that part of the country from Pitcarmick in Perthshire.

Twice in the Scottish team, this black and white collie was described by Donald as "a topper of a steady dog with plenty of power." Along with Corrie, another son of Garry, Coon was third in the National doubles competition.

The last time I visited Donald on his 170-acres of hill and 30 acres of arable on the hills beyond Bonar Bridge at Ausdale I became re-united with old Wiston Bill, winner of the 1970 International Trials at Kilmartin in David McTeir's hands and then given by his owner J. M. Wilson to his good friend, Donald. Donald and old "Willie" as he called him got on famously in the early 1970's and the pair lifted the Hebridean championship which was decided in Skye, Lewis and Harris.

156

Though I have seen various types of dogs working sheep and cattle, it was while at Donald's homestead that I first saw an Alsatian gather and separate sheep. "He is very wise and can do nearly all the sheep and cattle jobs," said Donald who had the Alsatian, named Whoopie, on the 'stop' whistle.

"I can be down working in the sheep fanks and perhaps forget to shut the gate. He would stand there all day and not a sheep would get past. He was also very easy to teach in the driving of sheep. He is a sensible dog and when we started I would walk beside him and tell him to walk. Then I would just slip behind him and he started off himself."

Whoopie found a lamb during the 1974 lambing. A young ewe had left her lamb on the hill. "I knew she had lambed in the morning and must have left the lamb somewhere," said Donald. "I could not find the lamb, but I took the big dog with me. He is a grand dog at finding anything which is lost and I kept him in the wind and he found the lamb in no time. So he saved that lamb's life."

About the only thing Whoopie could not do was talk. And if old Ben Nevis could only talk about the kindly Lochaber folk he watches over he would have something to say of Argyle Lawrie. They had each other's company and theirs alone many a summer morning long before daylight stirred this northern mountainland.

When the car lights flickered out of the black, round the side of Beinn Bhan, skirted along Loch Lochy, swung over the Caledonian Canal and headed up past Spean Bridge's commando memorial, old Ben knew that his 3 a.m. or 4 a.m. companion in these days in the 70's was Argyle Lawrie and that he would soon sweep past the mountain's feet, bound for distant places and sheepdog trials.

The A60 car he had when I called at his abode showed a remarkable 120,000 mileage. (My own had amassed 133,000 in three years). A muckle lot of miles for a shepherd but easy to understand when it is realised he could chalk up 400 miles on a summer Saturday.

Miles figured prominently in a crack with Argyle that night in the warmth of a Spean Bridge bar. There were fifteen to begin with for him each morning at that time just at daylight. On a single track road from the bothy at Achnacarry to the head of Loch Arkaig. But this one in the comfort of an estate mini-bus and with the company maybe of four other shepherds and twenty dogs. When the van stopped there was a parting at the head of the loch about Glendessary. Each shepherd made to his own hirsels, part of the Locheil estate of the Chief of Clan Cameron.

Argyle, with 1,500 ewes out to the tups when I called, headed far out on ground, mostly around the 3,000 ft level, through Glen Pean for a long solitary darg, twelve miles long, round the 2,700 ft. Carn Mor to near the waters of Loch Morar and a view over the quiet west with a sighting of Rhum, Eigg and Muck on a good day.

After a daylight-to-dark stint during which he walked twenty-five miles among the wintry white-dressed hills to turn small batches of ewes to the rams, Argyle told me: "You get used to it. This is the time of the year when I do most walking. Usually it is about twenty-five miles there and back each day during the tupping time when I have to bring these scattered lots of ewes to the tups."

There were fifty-five tups out on his own ground. "The ewes go in small puckles here and there and there may not be enough for the tup to stay with them. So it means going round the outside every day, turning them in. We need all these tups for the amount of ground they have to cover.

"It is on these far-out hirsels where it is not so heavily stocked that all the work is. There is plenty for the dogs to do just now. At lambing time on these places you just have to go about cannywise. Sheep are wild and sometimes not used to seeing people and you have to watch how you go about them. You need a dog that can get away quietly and not disturb them without too much fuss putting him out. They must be able to get well out and keep well off the sheep, giving them time to draw out from the rocks. You have to have a really good-going dog using his eyes."

Argyle had several of that mettle. They also had to be good travellers. One Saturday not many years ago he started the car at 4 a.m., was in Stirling for the trials there at seven o'clock and ran his entries. He headed north for the Atholl and Weem event near Pitlochry, ran his dog there and immediately left for Rogart in Sutherlandshire where he got due reward for his trip by lifting the championship. He was home that night at 11 p.m. "It is not so bad when you are coming home with something," he told me.

Another day saw him down at Skipness in Kintyre for his start to the day then back up country to get away through Dalmally, Tyndrum and Crianlarich to run at Callander. And from there he drove on to compete at Aboyne.

I knew another 'herd who also worked from 3 a.m.-12 midnight and whose good lady walked into the kitchen one Sunday morning to see their small daughter at breakfast. "Jeannie, dae ye ken whit time yur faither got hame last nicht," she queried the child. "Na," says Jeannie "but when a' cam doon fur m' breakfast his coat wis still swinging' back an' forrit on the peg!"

Perhaps Argyles best known collie was Bob, a mostly black dog he was bought as an eight week old pup. He was last in a litter off Tom Wilson's Sweep, son of the 1955 supreme, J. M. Wilson's Bill, and Lassie, a daughter of David Young's Dusk with Knight's Gael and Allan Jones' Roy blood. Bob was a sound sensible worker at trials and very pliable on the courses and on his home ground in that historic airt.

In another northern vale, legend has it that in the clearance of quiet Strath Carron a battle was fought beside the river near Gruinards. The victors will be recorded somewhere in our history books, but they were superceded on that same soil by other champions—the most northerly collies ever to win the brace (doubles) title at the Scottish National Sheep Dog Trials.

They followed the plough of John Campbell on the very land where that battle was said to have taken place. And when I first called there back in 1971 one of them was out on the heather hill beside Gruinards farm long before the Highland daylight had lifted, to seek tups for the cast sale at Dingwall.

It was only the previous year that his everyday work at that time among 250 Blackface ewes and 40 cows made him think of entering the brace class at the National for the first time. "If a man goes gathering, he is maybe working two dogs on the hill—and what is the difference in working them on the trials field," he told me.

So six year old Nell, a buy-in dog from Invernessshire and five year old Cap, whose future once rested between being a cattle dog or an even grimmer fate, gained for the Ardgay farm manager the National pairs title at the 1970 Haddington event and he went on to finish third at the same year's Kilmartin International to give the north a worthy name-maker to start off the '70's. John was later to become one of the most respected and consistent doubles runners in the sheepdog business and gained the International supreme brace title as well as representing Scotland in the singles. Good going for a man, who like a lot of north handlers, can manage to only a few trials before the National compared with the fair-sized programme southerly folk have traipsed to by then.

John had acquired the rough-coated black and white Nell from Alastair Munro, Dell of Inches, Inverness. One of the reasons for the purchase was the wealth of breeding—a line that became much sought after later in that decade and started off the 80's with another supreme champion in Tom Watson's Jen. Nell was off W. Hunter's Wiston Ben 111 which goes back to his Wilson's Mirk, McDonald's Spot and Purdie's Tam and is out of Cockburn's Nell which has the blood of Renwick's Roy, Cockburn's Mist and Wilson's Tweed and Mirk.

Caithness was the airt from which John acquired Nell's championship partner Cap, a son of Gilchrist's Spot. He is out of Douglas Hall's Kim, a tricoloured rough-coated daughter of McTeir's Mirk and Cockburn's Queen.

There will be more internationalist dogs to come from this land of the north. William Cormack put Caithness on the map with his rousing Scottish National victory at Dundee with the lithe white and black June which is featured elsewhere in this book and Sandy Campbell from nearby Bardnaclaven with his Hemp blood is one for the future, having already gained a Scottish 'cap,' and a national driving title. In Caithness too we have such worthy handlers as Charles Georgeson who, when I was at his farm in 1969, hunted his collies out right to the edge of the silent Dubh Lochs.

Here among peat thought to be probably the deepest in Scotland there is hidden danger from the lochs—deep bogland pools where in May and June the bog-bean entices the sheep into the lochans.

At that time Charles Georgeson had 2,000 acres deep into this Caithness moorland, a type of hill farm country vastly different from that which we southerners know. Nearly all moorland, his hefts ran out right to the Dubh Lochs. He lessened the danger to sheep through re-seeding 100 acres which the sheep preferred for grazing.

Charles had a spell on the Ayrshire/Galloway borderland and was 3½ years manager of a dairy estate near Berwick before returning to the Pentland Firth county. He took back with him to his native Caithness, Ben, a collie bred by his late brother. This was the dog which brought him moderate success when he first started in trials. On one side Ben went back to the dogs of Sutherland Banks of Bower, breeder of two of the breed's finest sires, Little's Spot and Little's Cap which were both trained by Johnny McIvor.

Back up to the north again just recently has gone one of today's 'characters', John A. MacLeod who is simply 'Jiy A' to those who know him. He is another of these hardy souls who seem to thrive on the massive hard North 'herdings with their vast sweeps of sheep and deer terrain.

There was, for instance, the 27,000 acres he once managed at Kinlochewe, Wester Ross. And an Argyllshire herding on wild rock country rising to more than 3,000 ft. Or again, the Blackface hefts at Glen Isla, one of the highest herdings in East Perthshire, going to the top of the Devil's Elbow. And then he came down to within a dog-length of Loch Lomond at Culag, near Luss where he bided for several years tackling grim, steep, unbending ground before taking the north road again in 1980.

There will be a hefting instinct no doubt in 'herds themselves to entice them repeatedly to these kind of charges. But those who know John A. MacLeod best as a devoted sheepdog man know only half his yarn. He had added 'masterpieces' as he termed them, in fox-hunting and stalking.

While manager and head striker with the Willis family, he stalked with royal personages of our own land and others from Eastern countries. And with the help of two terriers named Bengie and Sporran and a .270 telescopic rifle he accounted for more than sixty foxes in the summer of 1968 in West Sutherlandshire alone.

He was on a Cheviot charge then at Savalbeg above Lairg, a home he left to go on trials safaris from Mey to Newton Stewart, a circuit he continued once he came to Loch Lomondside and one no doubt he will be carrying on wherever he lands.

It was the skill of black, bare-skinned Glen which first took this Lochaber-born handler into the Scottish team at Stirling in 1955—seven years after he had started out in sheepdog circles from his father's farm near Lochailort, west of Fort William.

Glen was to do it another three times. Great grandfather of Wiston

Cap, Glen was off Wilson's Glen and Kirkland's Meg and was bought by John from Peeblesshire's John Richardson. Glen was third in the Scottish team in 1957, third in the International supreme and also at the big Hyde Park tourney in London. Two years later he won the Shepherd's Championship at the Scottish National event in Paisley, but the clock beat him at the International.

It took a while for John to get back on the International trail but in the middle 70's he became very well dogged again and was a force to be reckoned with. Back in 1969 when I looked in on John at Lairg he had the thirteen-month-old Ben which had begun in nursery trials in Dumfriesshire with Scott Anderson. He was off Thomson McKnight's tan and black Jaff—it was a tragedy when this promising collie died early in life—out of Willie Cuthbert's Fay which had Whitehope Cap blood. Ben brought in the prizes for John and to augment what became one of the best kennels at the time there was another Dumfriesshire purchase, Cap, from Kenny Gibson of Canonbie. Then Tweed came on to the scene too to pick up a big dose of prizes.

There was another Tweed which made the news in the north, the rough-coated black and white collie which helped Allan Gordon to win the first Highland League championship.

The North-East has long had a reputation for its able sheepdog men through the counties from Aberdeen to Inverness and the late 1970's drew new interest. But at the start of the decade and during its run, Allan Gordon was one of the crack handlers, and his Tweed was among those which earned him his reputation. In 1969 no collie won more open trials in Scotland than Tweed who was then six years old.

He was one of the brand that often came to the summit—a service pup. In other words, given over free for the stud fee. Allan at the time had Bill 11 and put him to Norrie Gordon's Tib from Glass to produce her first litter which included Tweed. Tib was a grand-daughter of Bonella's Moss. Through Bill 11, Tweed's bloodline took in Tom Johnstone's Hemp, Andrew Ainslie's Meg, J. M. Wilson's Moss and Jim Walker's Jim and Nell. Bill 11 once gained four trials victories in a week.

As it went into the 80's Scotland's sheepdog trials sphere was perhaps seeing another bulge of interest in the north-east corner. For several years, apart from a few noted prizelifters, the interest there seemed to have been waning, but a goodly number of new names were coming to the fore again. Fife, Kincardine, Angus and the counties further up nearer the right hand corner were again showing a keen interest in the business. The Highland men, as can be seen in their representation at National level, are well able to hold their own nowadays.

STRANGERS ON THE HILL

*The Border Collie, the pastoral world's traditional working dog is one of
the mainstays of the livestock industry in the U.K. But occasionally a
traveller comes across other types of stock dogs.*

We have with us now on our upland tracts an incomer—the Huntaway,
the barking forceful dog which has no equal in the vast back country of
sheep-dominated New Zealand.

Ironically its importation and spread throughout the U.K. is only
returning the blood which went out from the western regions of Scotland
with the early settlers to merge with other strains in the musterers' kennels
of the long green island 'down under.'

But the Huntaway is not alone in breaking the domination of the
smooth, medium and rough-coated Border Collie for my tramps amid hill
men have many times brought the pleasure of seeing able beardies—the
bewhiskered, hair-faced, long-wooled collie strain—and also stumpie-tails,
merles and even a full-blooded Australian Kelpie. Clever workdogs all of
them.

There is a tale they tell to this day in the long glens splaying out from
the Big Cheviot about the coming of the working beardies to this airt
where the rolling hill ribs fuse on the Scottish-English border.

Dealers, they will tell you, were up in the north to buy renowned
easy-fattening cattle beasts from the Highlandmen. They took a fancy to
a dog, a beardie which had been spotted working at one homestead. And,
as dealers, they were liberal with their offers. But the owner would not
sell.

The beardie mysteriously vanished from his Highland home. Today
around Yetholm, Wooler and other townships where the dialect of the
Cheviots is spoken, there are still working beardies. Strange country for
them when one considers some of the snow drifts of winter and the effect
it has on long-coated hill dogs.

But there are ways to beat it too. Some rub the dogs legs with
vegetable oil.

From high-lying Calroust cottage at the top of Bowmont Water near
Yetholm the beardies once went out right to the English border at 1,800
ft. For twenty years they were at the heels of Robert Brown the former
head shepherd there. They also followed at the hooves of his garron
during his shepherding rounds.

Robert tended some 1,100 ewes, 300 hoggs and the rams on hirsels totalling between two and three thousand acres when he had the post at Calroust which was later to be filled by the McMorran family, one of the best known in the sheepdog trials business locally and nationally.

An attractive member of Robert's collie team when I was at the homestead in 1971 was the ten year old merled Craig whose progeny could be found in many Border homes and as far afield as Speyside, Inveraray and Wiltshire. He was bred in the Framlington direction over the border in Northumberland and it is thought his forerunners could be linked to the Rogerson's Betty blood. At work then, he was accompanied by the blue beardie, Shep.

I often wonder what befell a youngster which was shaping well at the time, the half-beardie, Rob. "I like the half beardies," said Robert. "With the full beardie you have to wait on them and be patient before they are ready to train for work but the half-beardie comes on a bit quicker."

Craig was a powerful dog, good for cattle work and at dealing with trough-fed hoggs. His master reckoned the beardies would never baulk at any work and had tremendous 'eye'—the unseen power of domination and authority a collie holds over the sheep he is working. A regular demand for progeny of his dogs was credited to their ability to pass on power and force when handling sheep.

Beardies could soon get into difficulties in fresh falling snow through the length and weight of their coats. Tom Muirhead's answer was to skim over their legs with the hair clippers and then rub in oil. Shepherd over the moss-hags at Birkcleugh in Duneaton Water near Crawfordjohn, Lanarkshire for seventeen years when I visited him, he had never had any other type of dog on his run of thirty-one score Blackface ewes. Bonny dogs too, It was a great sight to see his line-up of shaggy-coated workers—grey Nap, the black and tan Meg, brown Fly, black and tan Sally and grey, white and tan Gyle—kenneled at the back of his cottage.

It was not their appearance, however, which ensured their continual presence at Birkcleugh. "My dogs are just for working on the hill and nothing else," said Tom. "They are grand hill dogs. I prefer them to the other ones any day. They have style and yet they are on their feet all the time. On a big drove they will be hard to beat."

Tom had first seen beardies working nearby in the same glen for a Skye man Lachie McDonald. From Lachie he acquired Nan, semi-retired when I saw her and enjoying the comforts of a house collie.

Tom usually took three of the beardies to the hill in the morning and two in the afternoon. "They can go longer than the ordinary collie, at least the majority of them. They are hardier and will not give in. I have never seen Nap beaten, for instance. They might not be just as quick at running out for their sheep but they will certainly cast out wide and they are steady and canny to work. At lambing time I can drive a single ewe and her lamb with no bother. You can let these dogs away and once they are round sheep you can leave them and go on to another heft. The

163

beardies will bring on the first lot of sheep to you no bother."

All Tom's beardies were trained on the farm. Perhaps a bit slower to break than regular hill dogs, they were sometimes trained by working on ducks. Part of the training was educating them to bark. "I like them to bark, not on the hill, but if sheep are dour to shift then I might make them bark. Sheep will shift quicker to a bark than if the dog was laid on too severely. Usually when I start them to bark around the pens I can do it by clapping my hands to teach them," said Tom.

In addition to clipping the dogs legs in snow conditions, Tom usually sheared the long coats off them in the spring and found that in a couple of months the hair had re-grown. "But they are odd looking for a while."

Oddity, however, does not mean ineffectiveness as I saw during the 1977 winter when I travelled to Atholl Forest to see more unusual dogs—stumpie-tailed barkers, probably blooded back to the old wise dogs of the west and with noise a-plenty to shift a bulk of Blackface when asked by a 'ho-ho' command.

On 20,000 acres of red deer territory the brindle and tan hunting dog Moira, capable of keeping 1,500 sheep moving over the heather ground and brainy enough without orders to clear any blockage of stock in the narrow drift to the buchts was a premier worker for John Murdoch.

Two good weiring dogs and a good hunter sets a man well for the high, rough ground, according to John, who was then the single-handed 'herd at Calvine where rakes, carrying 1,120 ewes among heavily populated red deer, run to the heights of Sron a' Chleirich only a few hundred feet below the bottom end of the Grampians.

Stumpie working dogs are scarce on the ground. Hunter collies—along with the bracken cutter and the girdle once the most useful tools of the trade in the rugged western ewe runs—have also nearly vanished. Folks have realised it too late and like some of the beef cattle breeds and the Clydesdale, maybe something across the water—in this case the New Zealand Huntaway—holds the answer to survival.

There are still those though, like John Murdoch, holding great store by the hunter. "I would not try to do my work without one. It is on the real steep rough ground that the hunters come into their own," he told me on my visit to Calvine. He herded then on ground rising from Glen Garry across General Wade's old road and going back some nine miles or so into the mountains heading through the Mealls and Allts eventually to Speyside.

On what was once two and a half hirsels over a lot of heather and moss and many corries at the back, the intriguing servant then was Moira, a four year old stumpie of brindle, tan and blue colouring. "She will almost certainly be one of the old Argyll hunting kind, or even from the islands. She is very noisy and great for droving jobs, gathering in hot weather and shifting big musters of sheep. I would not like to be without her," said John, who has now left the high ground.

164

Moira was bred by his cousin Robert Sorley, a 'herd in the Connel Ferry/Loch Etive district who had her mother. She was not a stumpie. Little was known about the sire but he was not a stumpie either.

An early starter, Moira was chasing and barking at four months old. "I kept her at it and that is why I think she has retained her barking ability," said John who has had experience of collies from hunter parents losing their bark and inclining towards 'eye.' "With hunters the thing is to keep them going when they cannot catch up on beasts. That is what makes them bark and so it becomes a habit. You really have no flanking commands. It is a case of sending her out for the sheep and stopping and giving her commands to bark at certain places."

John's orders for Moira to bark—collies are penalised for any noise at sheepdog trials—were either two or three sharp whistles, or, a traditional old west coast and islands call 'Ho-ho.'

So Moira was out most days on the far-stretching rakes—somewhere around six miles by nine miles—which John herded when I looked in to see his dogs. The sheer extent of the area meant in many instances getting to certain vantage points by Land Rover and using the telescope a lot.

Hunters with bark are used to get the sheep moving and the weirers—weiring dogs—are used, closer at hand. "With two good weirers and one good hunter you can go anywhere—you are well set if you have high ground," said John.

Determined not to lose Moira's qualities he purchased a dog of hunting type to mate to the bitch. The dog, Bob, a black and white smooth-coated collie, left seven pups. Five were stumpie and two had full tails.

Bob himself had a fair bark in him as I heard when he worked some of the Calvine tups around the feeding troughs. Lying in a strip between the busy A9 and the north rail line, the fanks were approached from the low fields by a six foot wide fenced run alongside the rail tracks. Sometimes between 400 and 500 sheep had to be pushed at one time along this fairly lengthy pad and the flock leaders were inclined to baulk or halt at some burns. On her own Moira learned to nip to the fore-end of the packet of sheep, run up close to them and bark them on their way so preventing any following hold-ups.

Her master has no fear of the barkers gripping or getting their teeth into sheep for, he said succinctly: "Barking dogs never grip or very rarely do so, I have found. When they are barking they cannot be biting."

Sheep, he said—and some of the old Forest ewes could be stern in defying weiring dogs—had also got to know about the bark. "When they hear the barking they start to draw away miles in front," he said. "The hunter's work is not so refined but as long as they are making a rumpus they are doing their work.

"The trouble is, hunters are out of date. Everybody was going daft on the trials ones for years and now they are needing these hunters in certain areas and there are few left."

165

About a month after my call to Calvine and not so far west over the mountains when doing an article at Barguillean, Taynuilt I came across what was then possibly the only full-blooded Australian Kelpie sheepdog working in this country.

He was working for head shepherd Robin Horne who did not know too much about the ancestry of the Kelpie, Corrie, but had been told by Australians who have seen it, that it is a Red Cloud Kelpie.

Corrie's pregnant mother was imported to Scotland about ten years previously. At Barguillean he was known as a 'perpetual motion' and it was impossible to get him to stand still for a photograph. The rust-coloured curly-tailed dog impressed me with his kindness and canniness when drawing in and working the Barguillean ewes on a farm which is a model for hill reclamation and back-country access and roads.

Historians say the Kelpies, renowned for natural ability to handle stock with a cautious approach, are descended from Scottish dogs. The Working Kelpie Council, a national organisation formed by Australia's foremost working Kelpie breeders, says the working Kelpie originated from the import of 'North Country or Fox Collies' in the late 1860's from Scotland.

Like sheep and cattle breeders there could be an environment and a place for each working dog breed, though the Border Collie to my mind, is unapproachable as the all-round craftsman.

But I have to admit, of all the sheepdogs I have ever seen, one of the most practical displays of sheer initiative and purpose came from a black beardie sent repeatedly to the hill on the McLaren family's grand stock farm of the Craig, Dalmally when I was gleaning information for an article on the farm there and Blackface sheep had to be brought down for photographing. Yet this impressive worker had not shown any sign of working until he was four years old—and in his background, not many generations back if my memory serves me right, was Labrador blood!

There are now many farms with Huntaways or Huntaway blood. Expert sheep shearer Brian Davis of Sennybridge was a pioneer in the 1970's of importing them from New Zealand and he was so pleased with this powerful, noisy breed that he got rid of his own Welsh and Scottish sheepdogs. They will never make a massive dent in the popularity or claim the premier role which the Border Collie has rightly claimed in this country but I am glad they have come to these shores.

Others may ask why we had to go to New Zealand when there are still left some of the old barking strains such as the stumpies, the hunters and also the Lakeland type cur which I have only seen at a distance on the fells. The more good working blood available the better.

THE NEW GENERATION

As we step warily into the century's last two decades, the scenery remains almost unchanged. But the people are changing. There are facets of rural and farming life where a change—which only means progress with its drawbacks and benefits—is accepted almost without notice. But when the structure and social backbone of the hills and its race of people begins to be breached, one does take notice. This is the reservoir of stock and man. It is the latter who are most important.

The land is swiftly losing its indigenous workers—those who follow the tasks of their fathers and their grandfathers. They are being replaced—where replacement is taking place considering the torrent of trees which in the previous decade has so vividly wiped hundreds of hirsels from the map—in many cases by the incomers.

Itinerants some of them, many with no experience of dog or stick before choosing their new life. Some of them naturally passing by under the delusion that as drop-outs they have found their true calling. Only to be sadly awakened next morning to the reality of a profession which has no equal and which wants none of their kind.

But the incomers also include men—and women—of better and sturdier mettle. Youngsters who in their keenness bring something back which is leaving the hills—character. The message then, is that the hills will need the incomers to fuse into their traditions. Where they are productive and eager to learn the wise ways of their predecessors, they are being accepted. Acceptance means welcome.

I have met many of the incomers and have also sojourned long with youngsters of the indigenous school and I now know that both can fit in to carry on the wonderful tradition of hill shepherding, something which for so many years was unbreached by those from outside.

There is a tremendous inspiration to be gained from looking back before taking the next step forward and so I often return to a valued book—once owned and signed by John Dickson, the shepherd-poet from Tweedsmuir—called *Herding a Hill Hirsel.*

The book was published in 1929 by *The Scottish Farmer* and brought together essays from a competition—restricted to shepherds or farmers herding their own hirsels—which aimed to obtain a record of the practical experiences of men who had been or were bona-fide engaged in shepherding the upland tracts.

The winner of the competition, William Little, a shepherd at Westruther Mains, Gordon, Berwickshire, reviewed his whole year's work in great detail and summed up the good shepherd like this: "Herding is not like any other occupation. On some hirsels where disease is bad, the more the shepherd does the less he has to show for it. He must be honest, careful, and above all, calm-tempered. A good-tempered man and a close-mouthed dog will do the work much more quickly and quietly than a noisy man and dog. It is not by walking much or seeming to do much that the shepherd proves himself a good one. It is by walking so as to disturb the sheep as little as possible, and by doing at the time what should be done."

Mr Little, penning words on the benefits of learning young, wrote: "If a man is to make an experienced shepherd he must begin early. The boy of eight or ten years who goes round the hill with his father, who went as a boy with his father, has a better chance of becoming efficient than the one who begins later in life. As he grows older he will be learning the habits of the sheep—how they go out and in (to the hill pasture) through the summer, and how the wind changing in winter causes them to seek shelter. He will learn how and when to hound his dog, how to feed a hungry lamb, how to drive in a keb (a ewe with a dead lamb) and how to skin and bury the dead. All the time he will be listening to shepherd lore that has been handed down from father to son for generations.

"With such an upbringing, how can he fail to become a good shepherd? Especially if along with all this he has imbibed a high ideal of duty, which, after all, is the greatest essential in how to herd a hill hirsel."

While writing a great deal so knowledgeably about good shepherding, Mr Little was also very telling when he wrote about the opposite aspect—of the shepherd who did what never should be done among hill sheep, who was irregular in his habits, going away to the hill at any time; hounding his dog and driving the sheep forcibly in taking near cuts himself; missing awalt (overturned) ewes, perhaps finding them dead the next time he went back; carelessness in turning the sheep out and in, and neglect in cleaning dirty ewes and lambs till they got broken with maggots, and the flies tormented them so that they could not graze in peace. These were all things which should not be done.

Mr Little added these paragraphs about bad shepherding: "When clipping time comes round, the careless shepherd hurries to the hill to gather, probably misses some, has to go back for the remainder—thus wasting precious time and making a confusion generally. Then he brings them through burns and bogs, and they arrive at the fold wet and heated. After the clipping he may not go to the hill for a week, and flies get leave to work their will on the cuts that may have occurred on clipping day. He neglects to see if all the lambs are mothered after clipping. A lamb not finding its mother will soon lose condition, and be a small one when sale time comes round. Neglect of foot rot will have the same result. The animals will only be fit to be classed as shotts, if allowed to go crawling about on their knees.

"Dipping is also rushed. Sheep are hurried too quickly through the dipping trough, with the result that the keds are not killed, and all the work of dipping and the dip itself is wasted. Rushing sheep through folds, filling buchts too full, so that they get heated and squeezed, should never be done, as it is sure to cause death.

"The shepherd who neglects to turn the sheep out to the high ground in the Autumn will find the grass scarce on the low ground when the winter storms come. In tup time carelessness in turning sheep together, having too many tups in one cut so that they fight and chase one another, or too few in another cut so that they have too much to do, and failure to notice a tup not working—these items will result in a poor crop of lambs and a large percentage of eild (yeld) sheep at the end of lambing time.

"During the spring months in good weather, disturbing or hounding the sheep too much or neglecting to bring in thin ones so that they die of poverty, in snow, not turning them away from the stells quietly to graze, or when getting hay, allowing them to lie all day where they have been foddered—that is not the way to herd hill sheep. When lambing time comes round, neglect to udder-lock the gimmers (yearling ewes) may cause the death through hunger of a good few lambs. Not bringing thin ewes into a field to give them a chance to improve will result in their not being fit to nurse their lamb and perhaps in their dying. All that increases the loss on the hirsel.

"Going round the hill and not taking time to observe all that goes on; driving kebs or any that need looking after, so roughly that they lie down and never reach their destination unless carried there—that is not the way it should be done at all.

"Wild sheep are very difficult to drive when taking them away from the cut they go with. A short-tempered man and a noisy dog are nothing short of calamity then. Having to gather sheep to folds, and turn them up to find a ewe that has left her lamb, is the wrong way to go about it. The want of attention in setting on lambs, or any that will not let their lambs suck, will result in the milk going off the ewe and the lamb dying; rough handling of a ewe that is difficult to lamb may cause inflammation; dead ewes and lambs lying about unskinned and unburied are a temptation for dogs and foxes. These are a few other items that should never occur."

Mr Little concluded his essay: "At the end of lambing time when ewes get thin with nursing they should not be turned out and in roughly. It only takes a little more time and patience to wait on them drawing away themselves. A shepherd who gets into a passion and a hurry with his sheep acts at a great disadvantage when working among them at this time. Herded like this, the death-roll is heavy and the hirsel is entirely wasted—a poor return to the farmer for the money invested in it, and an eyesore to everyone who knows how to herd a hill hirsel."

These thoughts are still handed down today by many shepherding families to their youngsters. It is knowledge, too, which has to be learned by others, such as some of the young people I interviewed when doing a series 'Herding—the new Generation.'

The incomers at that time included Tony Iley, a former teacher, ex-pie-factory worker, broken to shepherding on a twice daily diet of beans and toast, hauled into a Texas jail during a 20,000 mile hitch-hike on the other side of the Atlantic, landing himself through the gift of the gab with a newspaper reporter's job in Canada where he found himself a charming wife, and then heard again the call of the hills.

At the time of the series in 1975 Tony had returned to shepherd thirty score of hill Cheviots and some park ewes on Dumfriesshire uplands where he had cherished and learned the craft which first intrigued him when, as a schoolboy, he saw a butcher's dog loading fat lambs onto a waggon.

"It is a mild form of insanity really," chuckled Tony, talking of 'herding. "But there is no better way of life in spite of all its disadvantages." The 'insanity' reference was, I think, in connection with the unsociable hours. "On a place like this where we have two separate lambings of the inbye flock and the hill stock, it means eight weeks out of our life. Oh yes, the satisfaction comes later. But whatever the weather you have to be there all the time and you cannot say, 'well, at least I'll get Sunday off.' "

At the time I interviewed Tony the average man's wage was being hoisted about in newspapers as being £55 a week. Shepherds in these days certainly were not getting that. "I do not know what a shepherd is worth, but surely he is worth the average," said Tony. "If you go into a pub and have a drink with the average man—if you can find one, that is—you will find he has very little responsibility and he has not the outlays such as all the clothing we need, the dogs and their feeding etc.

"My father, who is a power station worker told me he can get me a job in the station sweeping up and I would get £7 a week more than I am getting here. But you have also to take into account the quality of life and there is obviously no better life or I would not be doing this.

"You have a measure of freedom and the rural community is a community that is not matched by any other branch of life. You have a tremendous number of characters. Everyone you meet is a character and an individual and that is worth an awful lot. Yes, they are vanishing. You can afford to have this independence and this quality of life but you cannot really be absolutely impracticable about it. You have to have a reasonable standard of living.

"Young people coming into the job need a decent house, but a lot of them leave a lot to be desired. And they also want a decent wage. All these recruiting drives and what-have-you are very fine but if you want to recruit someone into a job there is one sure way to make it attractive—and that is housing and money. That has to be thought of even although you have this quality of life."

Tony, who had to give up herding on doctor's orders some years ago and turned to furniture making, admitted there was no substitute for being hauled round the hill as a shepherd's son. "People like myself miss a lot and so when we take a 'herding there is no one there to teach us and we are fumbling around in the dark until we learn by experience which might mean making mistakes before we can learn."

Brothers Alex and William Waugh exemplified the old craft's treasured ways. Their father had shepherded at Craigdarroch, near Sanquhar for 26½ years when I spoke to them in 1975. His forebears were shepherds away back into the legendary mists. So too were those of Mrs Waugh snr. Uncles and cousins were the same—all handed-down sheep tenders.

William and Alex could not recall thinking of any other career. William, elder of the two put things into another perspective which maybe pinpoints part of the reason why families like the Waughs are getting fewer. "Schools today are inclined to look down on the farming side of the community and do not encourage boys to take up that side of life. They would rather encourage them away from it so I think more must be done to reverse this.

"The attitude they have is that if you will not do for anything else, you will do as a farm worker. But with all the machinery and quality of stock on farms nowadays a worker has to be fairly well educated to understand these kind of things."

Both the Waugh brothers shepherded at Craigdarroch. Alex, queried on the absence now of the traditional career rungs to eventual farm tenancy or ownership by the one-time shepherd said: "It would be a very difficult job nowadays to do it—farms are so expensive to take over. Just look at the interest if you had to borrow money."

They both agreed on the benefits of being sons of a shepherd for they said the incomers were at a disadvantage in not having their type of background. "It can be a drawback," said Alex. "There are some things difficult to teach the newcomer. You can teach them so much, about vaccinating and dosing sheep and so on, but it is not easy to learn them to herd a hirsel and tell them what to look for."

"We were brought up with it in our young days," said William. "We were always among sheep, even long before we left school and during the holidays. There is a lot you can learn out of books as well, particularly about health, but that does not beat being brought up with it. Everything does not work out just as the book says it should."

They agreed, however, that there was room for productive incomers. Said William: "If they are keen to learn there is nothing to hinder them to fit in. But they have to be keen on the job and willing to learn from other people."

Alex added: "I have seen perhaps a boy coming here in the summer time who would like to tell you how to do the job. You get the other one who is keen to listen. The one running about trying to tell you how to do it is not much good. You always pick up something if you are listening to others and if you think it is a good thing you can try it."

171

But, it appears, few of the incomers will make the grade. "It's a depressing interview, isn't it," said Philip Blake twice. Or was it thrice when we talked about the shortage of shepherds, their training and the 'pathetic' intake of those who sought to acquire a sheep man's skills in the country's only full-time sheep management course at Kirkley Hall, the Northumberland College of Agriculture's unit of which Mr Blake is Principal.

"There are a lot of people who see a newspaper article or advert or hear about the sheep course here," said Philip. "They come from different backgrounds, perhaps ranging from twenty to thirty-five years old. They could be married, perhaps with a house on mortgage, sometimes have a family and they just want to get out of the rat race. They are prepared to accept less money, and farming is the thing for them. So they think. They are quite sure, as a result of something they have read or seen that it has got to be the sheep industry. So the husband says he will take the course. More than ninety-five per cent of them will not make the grade."

In fact, admitted Mr Blake, it could be even higher than ninety-five per cent. "If they are determined, our advice is to keep their mortgaged house and perhaps have their wives go out to work to make sufficient to keep up the payments. And when they go to a farm they should live in a 'digs' situation so that if they do not like it they can move back to the industrial situation where they were before. In fact we try to dissuade that type from taking the course and entering the industry.

"Of those we cannot dissuade I don't think more than one in ten will make the grade. Because they get such a shock when they realise what life on the farm is like, let alone life on an outbye farm. A week or a fortnight is more than enough for them.

"Those who stick it can be successful. But there is another danger and that is because these people have been, in some cases, highly intelligent people, they are not on the farm for many weeks before they think they are better than those who have been there for years and they start shouting their mouths off. This upsets the resident labour force and can create problems."

Philip Blake agrees that perhaps rural teachers—as instanced by the Waugh brothers comments—instil into youngsters the notion that farming is a job for those not competent to make it in other industries. He cites parents as well. And rather than go out to recruit from outside the industry he thinks what the industry should be doing is to make sure a higher proportion of those already there should get better training.

Maybe Tony Iley, who for many years sent me poems for *The Scottish Sheepdog Handler* had a message between the lines when he penned this piece which he titled 'Where All Herds Go.'

As I lay on my death bed,
Relations all forlorn
The doctor shook his head and said,
"He'll never see the morn."
With tear filled eyes they looked on me
And slowly left my side
But faces sad and darkened rooms
I never could abide.
Thought I, "This place is not for me,
It's Heaven or Hell I'll try"
I closed my eyes and counted ten
And left without a sigh.
So to the gates of Hell I went
And on the doors I beat
The girls were great and beer was free
But I couldn't stand the heat.
So up to heaven I made the trip
There weren't as many there
But angels said, "The lambing's good
And sheepdog judges fair."
"You'll get two pairs of buits for free
And dog food grows on trees
Every ewe rears triplets
And grass grows to their knees."
So off to meet the Boss I went
Thought I, "I might just hire
On condition that He lets me
Light a daily forest fire."
The bargain sealed, I took His hand
He paid me in advance
Well, conditions weren't all that bad
And you've got to take a chance.
We all ran dogs from dawn to dusk
And after, gathered round
To drink our fill and bundle up
The five pound notes we found.
Well, all was grand till one sad day
When rumour spread around
That down in Hell their wages
Had passed ours by a pound.
We called a union meeting
And refused to run at trials
Or bundle up the fivers
And a ban was put on smiles.
We pressed our claims with fervour

But the Boss He only sighed
"On earth, in Hell or up here
You're never satisfied."
So all you 'herds for ever
Before you leave the land
Count your gold in time well spent
And those who shake your hand.

Those of us whose paths take us regularly among upland folk become involved over the years, and involvement turns to concern at the ever-diminishing numbers of stock and people.

It is through such events as sheepdog trials, shows and other pastoral events that we can make the public aware of the importance of the hills, the stock, the dogs and, above all, the folk and their unique culture. Without them, the countryside would be so much poorer.

Glossary

Airt — area.
Awalt — overturned.

Back-aboot — isolated area.
Blashy — stormy.
Buchts — sheep pens. Also fanks or folds.
Buist — the brand on a newly clipped sheep.
Burnhead — the top of a glen.

Carry — the number of sheep on a hill farm.
Cowpie or coupie — a sheep on its back unable to move. Also awalt.
Cundy — a gap in a dyke to allow sheep to pass through (same as lunky).

Darg — a long walk.
Dibble — a tool for making holes for garden plants.
Dowser — a water diviner.
Draft ewe — a ewe sold at the end of her breeding life on the hills.

Eild or yeld — not pregnant.
Eye — the hypnotic power of collies to make stock move.

Fastness — a remote hill area.

Garron — a small type of horse.
Gather — a round-up of hill sheep.
Gleg — very able.
Gurried — worried.

Heft or cut — a small geographical area of a hill sheep unit, possibly demarcated by burn, hilltop or hillend.
Hirsel — a large area of the hill which can contain several hefts.
Hoggs — young sheep, between weaning and their first shearing.
Hurchins — Hedgehogs.

In-bye — low pasture ground.
Ingle — a cottage or farm fireside.

Jeuk — to dodge.

Keb — a ewe with a dead lamb.
Keb-hoose — an outhouse where an orphan lamb will be twinned on to a ewe which has lost her lamb.

Keds — blood-sucking insects which attack sheep.
Keekers — dogs which are always watching their masters for commands.
Kenning — the ability of a shepherd to know individual sheep and their background.

Lazy-beds — areas where potatoes were placed and covered with soil.
Lirk — a gap in the hills.
Louping ill — a sheep disease.
Lunky — a gap in a dyke which allows sheep to pass through (same as cundy).

Marking — castrating lambs and cutting their tails.
Mawks — maggots.

Neighbouring — when farmers help each other with such seasonal jobs as sheep shearing and threshing.

Pad — a hill sheep path.
Parrick — a small pen used at lambing time to hold a ewe and her lamb.

Scrapie — a sheep ailment resulting from skin mite.
Sheuch — a trench.
Shotts — the rejected or second-best animals after stock has been selected for breeding at home.
Stells — hill enclosures.
Stravaig — to wander.
Strong-gaun — strong-willed.
Sturdy — a brain disorder in sheep.

Tarns — hill lochs in the North of England.
Trysts — old-time stock markets and fairs.
Tuip — ram.

Udder-lock — to clip the wool surrounding a sheep's udder to make it easier for the lambs to suck.

Wedder, wether — castrated male sheep.
Weiring dogs — dogs which can 'weir' or hold sheep close together.

Yowes — ewes.

175